WHAT TO EAT NOW

weightwatchers

What to Eat Now

150 Recipes, Meal Ideas & More for Your First 12 Weeks on Plan

WEIGHT WATCHERS PUBLISHING GROUP

VP, Editorial Director **Nancy Gagliardi**

Creative Director **Ed Melnitsky**

Photo Director **Deborah Hardt**

Managing Editor **Diane Pavia**

Editorial Assistant **Katerina Gkionis**

Food Editor **Eileen Runyan**

Editor **Alice Thompson**

Production Manager **Alan Biederman**

Photographers **Alan Richardson, Dasha Wright, Rita Maas**

Food Stylist **Michael Pederson**

Prop Stylist **Debrah E. Donahue**

Design **Pentagram**

Art Director **Liz Trovato**

Editorial and art produced by W/W Twentyfirst Corp., 11
Madison Avenue, New York, NY 10010.

SKU# 81207 Printed in the USA

about weight watchers

Weight Watchers International, Inc. is the world's leading provider of weight-management services, operating globally through a network of company-owned and franchise operations. Weight Watchers holds nearly 50,000 weekly meetings worldwide, at which members receive group support and education about healthful eating patterns, behaviour modification, and physical activity. Weight-loss and weight-management results vary by individual. We recommend that you attend Weight Watchers meetings to benefit from the supportive environment you find there and follow the comprehensive Weight Watchers program, which includes a food plan, an activity plan, and a behavioural component. In addition, Weight Watchers offers eTools on **WeightWatchers.ca** and on Weight Watchers Mobile. For the Weight Watchers meeting nearest you or information about bringing Weight Watchers to your workplace, call 1-800-651-6000. Also visit us online at our Web site, **WeightWatchers.ca**, and look for ***Weight Watchers Magazine*** at your newsstand or in your meeting room.

couscous salad with smoked turkey and apples, page 87

contents

apple pie waffles, page 125

about our recipes

While losing weight isn't only about what you eat, Weight Watchers realizes the critical role it plays in your success and overall good health. That's why our philosophy is to offer great-tasting, easy recipes that are nutritious as well as delicious. We make every attempt to use wholesome ingredients and to ensure that our recipes fall within the recommendations of Canada's Food Guide for a diet that promotes health and reduces the risk for disease. If you have special dietary needs, consult with your health-care professional for advice on a diet that is best for you, then adapt these recipes to meet your specific nutritional needs.

To achieve these good-health goals and get the maximum satisfaction from the foods you eat, we suggest you keep the following information in mind while preparing our recipes:

Weight Watchers 360° and good nutrition

Recipes in this book have been developed for Weight Watchers members who are following Weight Watchers 360°. ***PointsPlus*** values are given for each recipe. They're calculated based on the amount of protein, carbohydrates, fat, and fibre contained in a single serving of a recipe.

- Recipes include approximate nutritional information; they are analyzed for Calories (Cal), Total Fat, Saturated Fat (Sat Fat), Trans Fat, Cholesterol (Chol), Sodium (Sod), Carbohydrates (Carb), Sugar, Dietary Fibre (Fib), Protein (Prot), and Calcium (Calc). The nutritional values are calculated by registered dietitians, using nutrition analysis software.
- Substitutions made to the ingredients will alter the per-serving nutritional information and may affect the ***PointsPlus*** value.
- Our recipes meet Weight Watchers Good Health Guidelines for eating lean proteins and fibre-rich whole grains, and having at least five servings of vegetables and fruits and two servings of low-fat or fat-free dairy products a day, while limiting your intake of saturated fat, sugar, and sodium.
- Health agencies recommend limiting sodium intake. To stay in line with this recommendation we keep sodium levels in our

recipes reasonably low; to boost flavour, we often include fresh herbs or a squeeze of citrus instead of salt. If you don't have to restrict your sodium, feel free to add a touch more salt as desired.

• In the recipes, a green triangle (▲) indicates Weight Watchers® Power Foods.

• *Stay on track* serving suggestions have a ***PointsPlus*** value of ***0*** unless otherwise stated.

• Recipes that work with the Simply Filling technique are listed on page 227. Find more details about this technique at your meeting.

• All ***PointsPlus*** values in this book are for one serving.

For additional information about the science behind lasting weight loss and more, visit **WeightWatchers.ca/science**.

Calculations not what you expected?

• You might expect some of the ***PointsPlus*** values in this book to be lower when some of the foods they're made from, such as fruits and vegetables, have no ***PointsPlus*** values. Most fruits and veggies have no ***PointsPlus*** values when served as a snack or part of a meal, like a cup of berries with a sandwich. But if these foods are part of a recipe, their fibre and nutrient content are incorporated into the recipe calculations. These nutrients can affect the ***PointsPlus*** values.

• Alcohol is included in our ***PointsPlus*** calculations. Because alcohol information is generally not included on nutrition labels, it's not an option to include when using the hand calculator or the online calculator. But since we use alcohol information that we get from our nutritionists you might notice discrepancies between the ***PointsPlus*** values you see in our recipes, and the values you get using the calculator. The ***PointsPlus*** values listed for our recipes are the most accurate values.

Shopping for ingredients

As you learn to eat healthier and add more Weight Watchers Power Foods to your meals, remember these tips for choosing foods wisely:

Lean Meats and Poultry Purchase lean meats and poultry, and trim them of all visible fat before cooking. When poultry is cooked with the skin on, we recommend removing the skin before eating. Nutritional information for recipes that include meat, poultry, and fish is based on cooked, skinless boneless portions (unless otherwise stated), with the fat trimmed.

Seafood Whenever possible, our recipes call for seafood that is sustainable and deemed the most healthful for human consumption so that your choice of seafood is not only good for the oceans but also good for you. For more information about making the best seafood choices and to download a pocket guide, go to **edf.org** or **www.mpo-dfo.gc.ca**. For information about mercury levels, seafood, and more you can visit **WeightWatchers.ca**.

Produce For best flavour, maximum nutrient content, and the lowest prices, buy fresh, local produce, such as vegetables, leafy greens, and fruits in season. Rinse them thoroughly before using and keep a supply of cut-up vegetables and fruits in your refrigerator for convenient, healthy snacks.

Whole Grains Explore your market for whole-grain products such as whole wheat and whole-grain breads and pastas, brown rice, bulgur, barley, cornmeal, whole wheat couscous, oats, and quinoa to enjoy with your meals.

Preparation and measuring

Read the Recipe Take a couple of minutes to read through the ingredients and directions before you start to prepare a recipe. This will prevent you from discovering midway through that you don't have an important ingredient or that a recipe requires time for marinating. And it's also a good idea to assemble all ingredients and utensils within easy reach before you begin a recipe.

Weighing and Measuring The success of any recipe depends on accurate weighing and measuring. The effectiveness of the Weight Watchers program and the accuracy of the nutritional analysis depend on correct measuring as well. Use the following techniques:

- Weigh food such as meat, poultry, and fish on a food scale.
- To measure liquids, use a standard glass or plastic measuring 250 ml (1 cup) placed on a level surface. For amounts less than 60 ml (¼ cup), use standard measuring spoons.
- To measure dry ingredients, use metal or plastic measuring cups that come in 60, 75, 125 and 250 ml (¼-, ⅓-, ½-, and 1-cup) sizes. Fill the appropriate ml and level it with the flat edge of a knife or spatula.
- For amounts less than 60 ml (¼ cup), use standard measuring spoons.

turkey scaloppine with asparagus,
page 59

how to use this book

What will your first 12 weeks on the Weight Watchers program be like? Exciting, invigorating, challenging, rewarding. We guarantee it will be all of these things, but we also think it should be delicious and not too complicated. That's where this book comes in.

Your First Month is a perfect introduction to cooking and eating on the Program: These simple recipes will introduce you to the ingredients and techniques that can make cooking at home a powerful and satisfying strategy for weight loss. Best of all, you can prepare all the dishes in 15 minutes or less, so you'll never feel overwhelmed.

As you progress, **Your Second Month** will offer you an even wider variety of flavours and ingredients to keep your meals varied and interesting, while taking just 20 minutes or less to prepare.

For **Your Third Month**, you'll enjoy more choices than ever as we turn up the culinary creativity with superb 30-minute recipes.

And nothing beats a great ending, so we've packed the last chapter, **Your Snacks and Sweets**, with wonderful snack and dessert goodies—all for a ***PointsPlus*** value of **5** or less—that you can turn to throughout your journey.

Looking for even more inspiration? We've also included valuable *stay on track* tips throughout each chapter, plus special features that can help new members deal with everything from shopping to cravings. Success never tasted so good!

Stock Up for Smart Eating

Your pantry can be one of your strongest allies in losing weight. Most of our recipes take advantage of kitchen staples you may already have on hand. Take an inventory, then plan a shopping trip to stock up on those essential ingredients that make quick, healthful meals and snacks a reality. And remember: You can enjoy almost all fresh fruits and vegetables for a ***PointsPlus*** value of ***0***, so be sure to keep plenty of your favourites on hand.

On Your Shelves

- Canned seafood (tuna, salmon, clams)
- No-salt-added canned beans (assorted varieties)
- Quick-cooking brown rice
- Assorted whole grains (quinoa, quick-cooking barley, bulgur, etc.)
- Dried pastas (assorted varieties)
- Whole wheat couscous
- Old-fashioned and quick-cooking oats
- Canned low-sodium chicken, beef, and vegetable broths
- Canned tomatoes, diced tomatoes, tomato paste, and tomato sauce
- Canola oil, olive oil, sesame oil, and nonstick spray
- Red-wine, white-wine, apple cider, and balsamic vinegars
- Brine-cured olives and capers
- Bottled roasted red bell peppers (not packed in oil)
- Fat-free and reduced-calorie salad dressings
- Fat-free salsa
- Pepper sauce
- Dijon mustard
- Prepared horseradish
- Ketchup
- Fat-free mayonnaise
- Soy, hoisin, and fish sauces

- Light (reduced-fat) coconut milk
- No-sugar-added preserves
- Peanut butter
- Low-fat baked tortilla chips
- Salt, pepper, and all common dried herbs and spices
- Onions
- Garlic and shallots

In Your Freezer

- Lean ground beef (7% fat or less)
- Lean beef, pork, and lamb (assorted cuts)
- Chicken (assorted cuts)
- Skinless turkey breast (cuts and ground)
- Sausage (assorted types)
- Canadian bacon and turkey bacon
- Fish and shellfish (assorted varieties)
- Reduced-calorie sandwich breads
- Whole wheat pitas
- Tortillas and wraps (assorted varieties)
- Reduced-calorie hot dog and hamburger buns
- Frozen vegetables (assorted varieties)
- Frozen unsweetened berries (assorted varieties)

In Your Refrigerator

- Lean low-sodium sandwich meats
- Fat-free and low-fat cheeses (assorted varieties)
- Parmesan cheese
- Tofu and tempeh
- Fresh fruits and vegetables (assorted varieties)
- Fresh herbs (assorted varieties)
- Fresh ginger
- Large eggs
- Fat-free egg substitute
- Skim milk
- Unsalted butter
- 5% cream
- 2% sour cream
- Plain fat-free yogourt (Greek and regular)

Baking Essentials

- All-purpose flour
- Whole wheat flour
- Cornmeal
- Granulated white, brown, and confectioners' sugars
- Honey, maple syrup, and molasses
- Unsweetened cocoa powder
- Baking soda and baking powder
- Dried fruits and nuts (assorted varieties)
- Vanilla extract

YOUR FIRST MONTH

—

Ready in 15 Minutes or Less

breakfasts

Eggs and Lox Scramble
Florentine Omelette
Egg-and-Cheese Burrito Roll
Quick Berry Blintzes
Figs with Greek Yogourt
Top-of-the-Morning Smoothie

lunches

Deli-Style Turkey Reubens
Ham-and-Swiss Panini with Red Pepper Mayo
Chicken-Tomatillo Quesadilla
Mediterranean Salmon Wraps
Easy Lobster Rolls
Flatbread Pizza with Smoked Salmon
South-of-the-Border Tofu Wraps
Lemony Hummus and Goat Cheese Pitas
Snappy Tex-Mex Shrimp Soup
Easy Pea Soup with Prosciutto
Spicy Gazpacho with Chopped Egg
Chinese Chicken and Edamame Salad
Summer Seafood Salad
White Bean and Mozzarella Salad

dinners

Peppered Filet Steak with Zucchini
Beef and Broccoli Stir-Fry
Thai-Style Beef Salad
Pork Chops with Cherry Pan Sauce
Pesto and Pepperoni French Bread Pizzas
Chicken and Rice Burritos
Polenta with Sausage and Peppers
Sweet-and-Savoury Cabbage Slaw with Smoked Chicken
Barbecue Turkey Sandwiches
Turkey Scaloppine with Asparagus
Grilled Sea Bass with Chili-Lime Butter
Tuna Teriyaki with Ginger Bok Choy
Balinese Salmon Salad
Grilled Shrimp Caesar Salad
Hoisin Mushrooms and Tofu
Portobello Cheeseburgers with Pesto Mayonnaise

eggs and lox scramble

serves 1

per serving

- 5 ml (1 tsp) unsalted butter
- ▲ 1 large egg
- ▲ 2 large egg whites
- ▲ 30 ml (2 Tbsp) skim milk
- Pinch salt
- 55 g (2 oz) lox or smoked salmon, chopped
- ▲ 1 scallion, thinly sliced
- ▲ 30 ml (2 Tbsp) fat-free sour cream

Melt butter in small nonstick skillet over medium heat. Whisk egg, egg whites, milk, and salt in small bowl until frothy. Pour egg mixture into skillet and cook 30 seconds. Add lox and cook, stirring frequently, until eggs are set, about 30 seconds. Remove from heat and garnish with scallion and sour cream.

Per serving (175 ml [3/4 cup] egg mixture and 30 ml [2 Tbsp]) sour cream): 241 Cal, 11 g Total Fat, 4 g Sat Fat, 0 g Trans Fat, 242 mg Chol, 680 mg Sod, 9 g Carb, 2 g Sugar, 0 g Fib, 26 g Prot, 121 mg Calc.

for your information

Instead of separating eggs for recipes, you can purchase a carton of egg whites from the dairy section of your supermarket. 30 ml (2 Tbsp) are equal to about one large egg white.

eggs and lox scramble

florentine omelette

serves 1

per serving

- ▲ **750 ml (3 cups) lightly packed baby spinach leaves (about 85 g [3 oz])**
- **1 garlic clove, sliced**
- **2 ml (½ tsp) Italian seasoning**
- **30 ml (2 Tbsp) water**
- **5 ml (1 tsp) olive oil**
- ▲ **125 ml (½ cup) fat-free egg substitute**
- **Pinch salt**
- **Pinch black pepper**
- **45 ml (3 Tbsp) shredded reduced-fat Italian cheese blend**

1 Heat spinach, garlic, Italian seasoning, and water in medium saucepan over medium heat, stirring occasionally, until spinach wilts, about 2 minutes.

2 Heat oil in large nonstick skillet over medium-high heat. Pour in egg substitute and swirl to cover bottom of pan. Sprinkle with salt and pepper and cook, stirring gently, until underside is set, about 30 seconds. Continue to cook 30 seconds more, lifting edges frequently with spatula to let uncooked egg flow underneath.

3 Spread spinach mixture and Italian cheese blend evenly over half of omelette; fold other half over filling. Slide omelette onto plate.

Per serving **(1 omelette): 175 Cal, 8 g Total Fat, 3 g Sat Fat, 0 g Trans Fat, 11 mg Chol, 623 mg Sod, 10 g Carb, 0 g Sugar, 4 g Fib, 18 g Prot, 248 mg Calc.**

egg-and-cheese burrito roll

serves 1

per serving

- 5 ml (1 tsp) canola oil
- ▲ 125 ml (½ cup) fat-free egg substitute
- 2 ml (½ tsp) chili powder
- 1 (25-cm [10-in]) whole wheat tortilla
- ▲ 30 ml (2 Tbsp) shredded low fat Cheddar cheese
- ▲ 30 ml (2 Tbsp) fat-free salsa

1 Heat oil in large nonstick skillet over medium heat. Add egg substitute and chili powder and cook, stirring frequently, until set, about 3 minutes.

2 Place tortilla between 2 paper towels and microwave on High until warm, about 20 seconds. Fill tortilla with egg mixture, Cheddar cheese, and salsa; roll up tortilla.

Per serving (1 burrito): 283 Cal, 9 g Total fat, 2 g Sat fat, 0 g Trans fat, 3 mg Chol, 882 mg Sod, 30 g Carb, 6 g Sugar, 2 g Fib, 20 g Prot, 220 mg Calc.

stay on track

Starting your breakfast with a juicy half grapefruit or peeled orange will give you a fabulous dose of fibre and vitamin C.

quick berry blintzes

serves 2

per serving

- ▲ **250 ml (1 cup) mixed berries**
- **10 ml (2 tsp) sugar**
- **5 ml (1 tsp) lemon juice**
- **1 ml (¼ tsp) cinnamon**
- **4 (17 cm [7-in]) ready-to-use crêpes**
- ▲ **90 ml (6 Tbsp) part skim ricotta cheese**

1 Toss 125 ml (½ cup) berries with sugar, lemon juice, and cinnamon in small bowl; set aside.

2 Preheat broiler. Spray baking sheet with nonstick spray.

3 Spread each crêpe with 22 ml (1½ Tbsp) ricotta, top with 30 ml (2 Tbsp) berry mixture, and fold closed. Transfer blintzes to prepared baking sheet. Broil until lightly browned and just heated through, 3–4 minutes. Serve at once, garnished with remaining 125 ml (½ cup) berries.

Per serving **(2 filled crêpes and 60 ml [¼ cup] berries): 299 Cal, 15 g Total Fat, 8.4 g Sat Fat, 0 g Trans Fat. 15 mg Chol, 331 mg Sod, 31 g Carb, 10 g Sugar, 3 g Fib, 12 g Prot, 163 mg Calc.**

for your information

If it's peach season, you might want to replace the berries with 500 ml (2 cups) diced peeled peaches.

quick berry blintzes

Figs with Greek Yogourt

serves 1

per serving

- 4 dried Calimyrna (golden) figs, stems removed, figs quartered
- 75 ml (1/3 cup) water
- ▲ 175 ml (3/4 cup) plain fat-free Greek yogourt
- 15 ml (1 Tbsp) chopped toasted walnuts
- 5 ml (1 tsp) honey

Combine figs and water in small saucepan and bring to boil over high heat. Remove from heat, cover, and let stand 5 minutes. Drain and place figs in bowl. Top with yogourt and walnuts; drizzle with honey.

Per serving (1 bowl): 243 Cal, 5 g Total Fat, 1 g Sat Fat, 0 g Trans Fat, 0 mg Chol, 71 mg Sod, 35 g Carb, 29 g Sugar, 4 g Fib, 17 g Prot, 177 mg Calc.

for your information

Dried figs are loaded with fibre and potassium, making them a great way to start your morning. Calimyrnas are a particularly plump and tender variety of dried fig, but you can use other varieties in this recipe; just make sure you let them soak long enough to become tender.

top-of-the-morning smoothie

serves 1

per serving

- ▲ **1 small banana, peeled and sliced**
- **2 pitted dates**
- ▲ **125 ml (½ cup) plain fat-free yogourt**
- **1 ml (¼ tsp) vanilla extract**
- **15 ml (1 Tbsp) unflavoured soy isolate protein powder**
- **15 ml (1 Tbsp) wheat germ**
- **4 ice cubes**

Place all ingredients in blender and puree. Pour into tall glass.

Per serving (1 smoothie): 254 Cal, 1 g Total Fat, 0 g Sat Fat, 0 g Trans Fat, 2 mg Chol, 159 mg Sod, 48 g Carb, 34 g Sugar, 5 g Fib, 15 g Prot, 259 mg Calc.

for your information

Protein isolate products are available at most supermarkets and also at natural foods stores and stores that specialize in nutritional supplements. They can be soy, dairy, or egg-white based or consist of a mix of these. They're a good source of protein and nutrients to add to beverages like smoothies.

deli-style turkey reubens

serves 2

per serving

- ▲ **4 slices reduced-calorie rye bread**
- **30 ml (2 Tbsp) reduced-fat Thousand Island dressing**
- **85 g (3 oz) sliced turkey pastrami**
- **60 ml (¼ cup) drained jarred pickled red cabbage, rinsed and squeezed dry**
- **2 (20-g [¾-oz]) slices low-fat reduced-sodium Swiss cheese**
- **5 ml (1 tsp) canola oil**

1 Spread 2 slices of bread evenly with dressing. Top each slice with half of pastrami, half of cabbage, and 1 slice Swiss cheese. Top sandwiches with remaining bread.

2 Heat oil in large nonstick skillet over medium-high heat. Add sandwiches and cook until bread is toasted and cheese is melted, about 2 minutes per side. Cut each sandwich in half and serve at once.

Per serving (1 sandwich): 289 Cal, 13 g Total Fat, 4 g Sat Fat, 0 g Trans Fat, 46 mg Chol, 838 mg Sod, 29 g Carb, 7 g Sugar, 6 g Fib, 17 g Prot, 23 mg Calc.

stay on track

These sandwiches are a little higher in ***PointsPlus*** value than some, but with plenty of protein and fibre they're bound to keep you satisfied all afternoon. If you like, serve them with unsweetened dill pickles to add a punch of flavour.

deli-style turkey reubens

ham-and-swiss panini with red pepper mayo

serves 1

per serving

- ▲ **15 ml (1 Tbsp) drained and finely chopped roasted red bell pepper (not packed in oil)**
- **15 ml (1 Tbsp) fat-free mayonnaise**
- **1 ml (¼ tsp) red-wine vinegar**
- **Small pinch cayenne**
- ▲ **2 slices reduced-calorie multigrain bread**
- ▲ **2 (20-g [¾-oz]) slices lean reduced-sodium ham**
- **4 large fresh basil leaves**
- **1 (20-g [¾-oz]) slice low-fat reduced-sodium Swiss cheese**

1 Combine roasted bell pepper, mayonnaise, vinegar, and cayenne in small bowl. Spread mixture on 1 slice of bread; layer with ham, basil, and Swiss cheese. Top with remaining bread.

2 Spray ridged grill pan with nonstick spray and set over medium-high heat, or heat panini sandwich maker according to manufacturer's instructions. Add sandwich. Cover with heavy skillet and grill until bread is well marked and cheese is melted, 3–4 minutes per side. (For sandwich maker, cook 3–4 minutes total.) Serve at once.

Per serving **(1 sandwich): 216 Cal, 7 g Total Fat, 4 g Sat Fat, 0 g Trans Fat, 35 mg Chol, 803 mg Sod, 26 g Carb, 5 g Sugar, 7 g Fib, 17 g Prot, 235 mg Calc.**

stay on track

Serve this toasty sandwich with 500 ml (2 cups) carrot, celery, and cucumber sticks and 30 ml (2 Tbsp) fat-free Italian dressing for dipping (the per-serving ***PointsPlus*** value will increase by ***1***).

chicken-tomatillo quesadilla

serves 1

per serving

- 1 (20-cm [8-in]) wheat tortilla
- ▲ 30 ml (2 Tbsp) shredded low fat Monterey Jack cheese
- ▲ 125 ml (½ cup) baby spinach leaves
- ▲ 125 ml (½ cup) chopped skinless roast chicken breast
- ▲ 30 ml (2 Tbsp) fat-free tomatillo salsa
- 2 ml (½ tsp) canola oil
- ▲ 15 ml (1 Tbsp) fat-free sour cream
- 15 ml (1 Tbsp) chopped fresh cilantro

1 Sprinkle half of tortilla with Monterey Jack cheese and then top with spinach, chicken, and salsa. Fold other half over filling and press down lightly.

2 Heat oil in medium nonstick skillet over medium heat. Place quesadilla in skillet and cook until bottom is crisp, 2–3 minutes. Flip and cook until other side is crisp and cheese is melted, about 2 minutes. Top with sour cream and cilantro.

Per serving (1 quesadilla): 386 Cal, 14 g Total Fat, 3 g Sat Fat, 0 g Trans Fat, 70 mg Chol, 668 mg Sod, 32 g Carb, 1 g Sugar, 6 g Fib, 33 g Prot, 186 mg Calc.

mediterranean salmon wraps

mediterranean salmon wraps

serves 2

per serving

- ▲ **1 (213-g [7½-oz]) can no-salt-added wild salmon, drained, skin and large bones removed and discarded**
- **6 small black olives (not packed in oil), chopped**
- **45 ml (3 Tbsp) fat-free mayonnaise**
- ▲ **30 ml (2 Tbsp) finely chopped red onion**
- **15 ml (1 Tbsp) capers, drained and chopped**
- **1 ml (¼ tsp) black pepper**
- ▲ **250 ml (1 cup) loosely packed mixed lettuce**
- **2 (20-cm [8-in]) wheat tortilla**

1 Combine salmon, olives, mayonnaise, onion, capers, and pepper in medium bowl and stir until salmon is flaked.

2 Place 125 ml (½ cup) lettuce on each tortilla and top each with half of salmon mixture. Roll up tortillas and cut in half diagonally.

Per serving (2 halves): 320 Cal, 13 g Total Fat, 3 g Sat Fat, 0 g Trans Fat, 49 mg Chol, 596 mg, Sod, 27 g Carb, 4 g Sugar, 2 g Fib, 26 g Prot, 320 mg Calc.

for your information

This is a delicious break from the usual seafood salad sandwich, and using fat-free mayonnaise and wild salmon makes it wonderfully healthful. Look for no-salt-added canned salmon and you'll also skip the high sodium found in most canned seafood.

easy lobster rolls

serves 2

per serving

- **45 ml (3 Tbsp) fat-free mayonnaise**
- ▲ **30 ml (2 Tbsp) finely chopped red onion**
- **15 ml (1 Tbsp) fresh lemon juice**
- **0.5 ml (1/8 tsp) black pepper**
- ▲ **200 g (7 oz) fully cooked frozen lobster meat, thawed and drained**
- ▲ **1 small celery stalk, finely chopped**
- ▲ **2 light whole-grain hot dog rolls, split and lightly toasted**

Combine mayonnaise, onion, lemon juice, and pepper in medium bowl. Cut any large chunks of lobster meat into small pieces. Add lobster and celery to bowl and toss to coat. Evenly fill rolls with lobster mixture.

Per serving (1 filled roll): 237 Cal, 3 g Total Fat, 1 g Sat Fat, 0 g Trans Fat, 73 mg Chol, 780 mg Sod, 29 g Carb, 7 g Sugar, 4 g Fib, 24 g Prot, 125 mg Calc.

flatbread pizza with smoked salmon

serves 2

per serving

- **5 ml (1 tsp) olive oil**
- **1 (25-cm [10-in]) whole wheat lavash bread**
- **45 ml (3 Tbsp) farmer cheese**
- **15 ml (1 Tbsp) prepared drained horseradish**
- **Pinch black pepper**
- ▲ **1 plum tomato, diced**
- ▲ **3 scallions, thinly sliced**
- **55 g (2 oz) thinly sliced smoked salmon or lox, cut into strips**
- **30 ml (2 Tbsp) chopped fresh dill**

1 Heat oil in large skillet over medium-high heat. Add lavash and cook, turning occasionally, until crisp and golden, about 4 minutes. Place on cutting board.

2 Combine farmer cheese, horseradish, and pepper in small bowl; spread evenly over lavash. Top with tomato, scallions, salmon, and dill. Cut in half.

Per serving (½ pizza): 223 Cal, 9 g Total Fat, 2 g Sat Fat, 0 g Trans Fat, 14 mg Chol, 448 mg Sod, 22 g Carb, 1 g Sugar, 3 g Fib, 12 g Prot, 106 mg Calc.

stay on track

Craving pizza? Try this satisfying quick-and-easy homemade pizza that uses a whole-grain crust and low-fat farmer cheese. Add a bowl of refreshing fruit to your lunch and you'll have a terrifically healthful and delicious meal.

south-of-the-border tofu wraps

serves 2

per serving

- ▲ **225 g (8 oz) package smoked tofu, diced**
- ▲ **125 ml (½ cup) diced red bell pepper**
- ▲ **2 scallions, thinly sliced**
- ▲ **60 ml (¼ cup) fat-free salsa**
- **30 ml (2 Tbsp) chopped fresh cilantro**
- **20 ml (4 tsp) fat-free mayonnaise**
- **2 (17.5-cm [7-in]) whole wheat tortillas**
- ▲ **2 romaine lettuce leaves**

1 Combine tofu, bell pepper, scallions, salsa, and cilantro in small bowl.

2 Spread 10 ml (2 tsp) mayonnaise on each tortilla. Top with tofu mixture and lettuce leaf. Roll up tortillas and cut in half. Serve at once, or wrap in plastic wrap and refrigerate up to 1 day.

Per serving (1 wrap): 209 Cal, 9 g Total Fat, 1 g Sat Fat, 0 g Trans Fat, 1 mg Chol, 491 mg Sod, 24 g Carb, 4 g Sugar, 12 g Fib, 18 g Prot, 239 mg Calc.

for your information

Firm, tasty smoked tofu has already been seasoned and baked, making it a convenient addition to salads and sandwiches. Look for it in the refrigerated section of most supermarkets.

lemony hummus and goat cheese pitas

serves 2

per serving

- ▲ 6 grape tomatoes, quartered
- ▲ 1 scallion, thinly sliced
- 15 ml (1 Tbsp) chopped fresh parsley
- 7 ml (1½ tsp) lemon juice
- 1 large (17.5-cm [7-in]) whole wheat pita bread
- 30 ml (2 Tbsp) hummus
- ▲ 250 ml (1 cup) loosely packed mixed lettuce
- 125 ml (½ cup) crumbled goat cheese

1 Combine tomatoes, scallion, parsley, and lemon juice in medium bowl; set aside.

2 Cut pita bread in half to form 2 pita pockets. Spread 15 ml (1 Tbsp) hummus inside each pocket.

3 Add lettuce and goat cheese to tomato mixture and toss to mix. Spoon evenly into pita pockets. Serve at once, or wrap in plastic wrap and refrigerate up to 1 day.

Per serving (1 pocket): 209 Cal, 8 g Total Fat, 5 g Sat Fat, 0 g Trans Fat, 13 mg Chol, 356 mg Sod, 26 g Carb, 3 g Sugar, 5 g Fib, 11 g Prot, 64 mg Calc.

snappy tex-mex shrimp soup

snappy tex-mex shrimp soup

serves 2

per serving

- **10 ml (2 tsp) olive oil**
- ▲ **½ onion, diced**
- ▲ **½ green bell pepper, diced**
- **1 garlic clove, minced**
- ▲ **250 ml (1 cup) canned no-salt-added diced tomatoes**
- ▲ **250 ml (1 cup) frozen corn kernels**
- **2 ml (½ tsp) chili powder**
- **1 ml (¼ tsp) salt**
- ▲ **225 g (½ lb) medium peeled and deveined shrimp**
- **30 ml (2 Tbsp) chopped fresh cilantro**

1 Heat oil in large saucepan over medium-high heat. Add onion, bell pepper, and garlic. Cook, stirring frequently, until softened, about 2 minutes.

2 Add tomatoes, corn, chili powder, and salt and bring to boil. Stir in shrimp; return to boil. Reduce heat and cover. Simmer until shrimp are just opaque in centre, about 4 minutes. Sprinkle with cilantro.

Per serving (about 375 ml [1½ cups]): 251 Cal, 7 g Total Fat, 1 g Sat Fat, 0 g Trans Fat, 168 mg Chol, 505 mg Sod, 27 g Carb, 7 g Sugar, 3 g Fib, 22 g Prot, 71 mg Calc.

for your information

If you like, use frozen diced onion and frozen diced bell pepper instead of fresh and save yourself a few minutes of chopping; the frozen vegetables will cook almost as quickly as fresh.

easy pea soup with prosciutto

serves 2

per serving

- ▲ **425 ml [1¾ cups) low-sodium chicken broth**
- ▲ **500 ml (2 cups) (225 g [8 oz]) frozen peas**
- ▲ **125 ml (½ cup) frozen diced onions**
- ▲ **125 ml (½ cup) cooked peeled, chopped potato**
- **4 thin slices prosciutto or other cured ham, diced**
- **0.5 ml (⅛ tsp) black pepper**

1 Combine broth, peas, onions, and potato in large saucepan; cover and bring to boil. Cook, stirring occasionally, until vegetables are tender, about 4 minutes. Remove pan from heat and let soup cool 5 minutes.

2 In batches, pour soup into blender and puree. Return soup to saucepan and reheat if necessary. Divide soup between 2 bowls and top evenly with prosciutto and pepper.

Per serving (425 ml [1¾ cups] soup and 2 slices prosciutto): 263 Cal, 5 g Total Fat, 1 g Sat Fat, 0 g Trans Fat, 22 mg Chol, 933 mg Sod, 36 g Carb, 9 g Sugar, 10 g Fib, 21 g Prot, 50 mg Calc.

for your information

If you don't have leftover cooked potatoes, you can use frozen diced potatoes or frozen potatoes O'Brien.

spicy gazpacho with chopped egg

serves 2

per serving

- ▲ ½ yellow bell pepper, coarsely chopped
- ▲ 1 Kirby (pickling) cucumber, peeled and coarsely chopped
- ▲ ½ small red onion, coarsely chopped
- ▲ 130 g (4½ oz) canned chopped green chiles, drained
- ▲ 1 (414 ml [4¼ fl. oz]) can no-salt-added diced tomatoes
- ▲ 250 ml (1 cup) reduced-sodium vegetable or chicken broth
- 7 ml (1½ tsp) sherry vinegar or red-wine vinegar
- 0.5 ml (⅛ tsp) cayenne, or to taste
- ▲ 2 large hard-boiled eggs, chopped
- 5 ml (1 tsp) olive oil

1 Place 2 soup bowls in freezer just before preparing soup.

2 Combine bell pepper, cucumber, and onion in food processor. Pulse just until finely chopped. Transfer to large bowl and stir in chiles, tomatoes, broth, vinegar, and cayenne. Divide soup between chilled bowls. Sprinkle each with egg and drizzle with olive oil.

Per serving (500 ml [2 cups] soup, 1 chopped egg, and 2 ml [½ tsp] olive oil): 189 Cal, 8 g Total Fat, 2 g Sat Fat, 0 g Trans Fat, 212 mg Chol, 286 mg Sod, 19 g Carb, 11 g Sugar, 4 g Fib, 9 g Prot, 99 mg Calc.

chinese chicken and edamame salad

serves 2

per serving

- 30 ml (2 Tbsp) orange juice
- 15 ml (1 Tbsp) lime juice
- 15 ml (1 Tbsp) reduced-sodium soy sauce
- 5 ml (1 tsp) Asian (dark) sesame oil
- 5 ml (1 tsp) grated peeled fresh ginger
- ▲ 250 ml (1 cup) diced cooked skinless boneless chicken breast
- ▲ 175 ml (¾ cup) frozen shelled edamame, thawed, cooked according to package directions if raw
- ▲ ½ red bell pepper, diced
- ¼ Hass (California) avocado, halved, pitted, peeled, and diced
- 30 ml (2 Tbsp) chopped fresh cilantro

Whisk together orange juice, lime juice, soy sauce, oil, and ginger in large bowl. Add chicken, edamame, and bell pepper; toss to coat. Add avocado and cilantro and toss again.

Per serving (310 ml [1¼ cups]): 236 Cal, 10 g Total Fat, 1 g Sat Fat, 0 g Trans Fat, 60 mg Chol, 324 mg Sod, 10 g Carb, 3 g Sugar, 4 g Fib, 27 g Prot, 46 mg Calc.

stay on track

For more veggie goodness, serve the salad over a bed of shredded carrot and cabbage tossed with lime juice.

chinese chicken and edamame salad

summer seafood salad

serves 2

per serving

- ▲ ½ (450-g [1-lb]) bag frozen seafood medley (shrimp, calamari, scallops, shelled mussels, and imitation crabmeat)
- ▲ 250 ml (1 cup) cherry tomatoes, quartered
- ▲ 125 ml (⅓ cup) fresh or frozen thawed corn kernels
- ▲ 75 ml (⅓ cup) chopped red onion
- ▲ 1 stalk celery, sliced
- 15 ml (1 Tbsp) lemon juice
- 10 ml (2 tsp) olive oil
- 1 ml (¼ tsp) salt
- 0.5 ml (⅛ tsp) black pepper

1 Bring large pot of water to boil. Add seafood and cook until thawed and just opaque in centre, about 2 minutes. Drain. Rinse under running cold water until cool. Drain again and transfer to large bowl.

2 Add tomatoes, corn, onion, celery, lemon juice, oil, salt, and pepper; toss to coat.

Per serving (500 ml [2 cups]): 196 Cal, 6 g Total Fat, 1 g Sat Fat, 0 g Trans Fat, 103 mg Chol, 518 mg Sod, 16 g Carb, 5 g Sugar, 3 g Fib, 21 g Prot, 56 mg Calc.

white bean and mozzarella salad

serves 1

per serving

- ▲ ½ (398 ml [14 fl. oz]) can no-salt-added cannellini beans (about 175 ml [¾ cup]), rinsed and drained
- ▲ 30 g (1 oz) part skim mozzarella cheese, sliced
- ▲ 1 small jarred roasted red bell pepper (not packed in oil), drained and coarsely chopped
- ▲ 1 small celery stalk, thinly sliced
- 15 ml (1 Tbsp) fat-free Italian dressing
- 2 ml (½ tsp) chopped fresh rosemary (optional)
- ▲ 500 ml (2 cups) sliced hearts of romaine lettuce

Combine beans, mozzarella, roasted bell pepper, celery, dressing, and rosemary, if using, in medium bowl and toss to combine. Arrange lettuce on a plate. Top with bean salad.

Per serving (250 ml [1 cup] bean salad and 500 ml [2 cups] lettuce): 311 Cal, 5 g Total Fat, 3 g Sat Fat, 0 g Trans Fat, 18 mg Chol, 619 mg Sod, 43 g Carb, , 7 g Sugar, 12 g Fib, 22 g Prot, 411 mg Calc.

stay on track

This great salad is packed with fibre, protein, and calcium to help you feel satisfied all day but still clocks in at only **5 *PointsPlus*** value. Try packing it up to take along as a brown-bag lunch to help you stay on Plan.

Situations/ Solutions

Losing weight can be challenging, but anticipating some of the situations you may encounter on a daily or weekly basis can be a big help. This section covers some common stumbling blocks and suggests some recipes in this book that can help you confront them.

It's 7 am and I'm not feeling particularly hungry.

Statistics show that eating breakfast can help prevent overeating later in the day, so try one of these light and easy breakfast recipes—ready in under 15 minutes:

Florentine Omelette, p 20, ***PointsPlus*** value: ***4***

Figs with Greek Yogourt, p 24, ***PointsPlus*** value: ***6***

Top-of-the-Morning Smoothie, p 25, ***PointsPlus*** value: ***6***

The delis and restaurants close to where I work don't have many healthful lunch options.

Visit a salad bar and pick up the fixings for our tasty White Bean and Mozzarella Salad, page 43, ***7 PointsPlus*** value. Or plan ahead and make one of our simple lunch recipes that can easily be packed and won't have you blowing your daily ***PointsPlus*** Target. These can be prepared in under 15 minutes:

Lemony Hummus and Goat Cheese Pitas, p 35, ***PointsPlus*** value: ***5***

South-of-the-Border Tofu Wraps, p 34, ***PointsPlus*** value: ***6***

Deli-Style Turkey Reubens, p 26, ***PointsPlus*** value: ***8***

It's 3 pm and dinnertime is soooo far away.

Keep these easy snacks on hand and enjoy them with one of your favourite ***0 PointsPlus*** value beverages:

Curried Vegetable Fritters, p 198, ***PointsPlus*** value: ***3***

Cranberry Tea Scones, p 206, ***PointsPlus*** value: ***4***

It's 5 pm. What's for dinner?

Many of our recipes can quickly be made from ingredients you probably have right in your pantry, fridge, or freezer. Here are three delicious options to try:

Beef, Black Bean, and Beer Chili, p 151, ***PointsPlus*** value: ***6***

Salmon Cakes with Dijon-Herb Sauce, p 104, ***PointsPlus*** value: ***6***

Pasta e Fagioli Soup, p 134, ***PointsPlus*** value: ***6***

Company's coming—I want to serve food everyone will love but don't want to blow my eating plan.

These recipes will please just about everyone and will make it easy for you to stick to your daily ***PointsPlus*** Target:

Savoury Tomato Bites, p 189, ***PointsPlus*** value: ***2***

Shrimp Cocktail Salads, p 186, ***PointsPlus*** value: ***3***

Filet Mignon with Red Wine and Herb Sauce, p 148, ***PointsPlus*** value: ***6***

Sicilian-Style Penne with Eggplant, p 182, ***PointsPlus*** value: ***8***

Dark Chocolate Soufflés with Raspberry Sauce, p 209, ***PointsPlus*** value: ***4***

Five-Spice Carrot Cake, p 204, ***PointsPlus*** value: ***5***

I'm heading to the movies tonight, and I need some help saying no to the oversized, overpriced foods at the concession stand.

Pack up a portion of one of these delicious treats:

Mocha-Walnut Biscotti, p 219, ***PointsPlus*** value: ***2***

Fruit and Spice Popcorn Mix, p 201, ***PointsPlus*** value: ***3***

Heavenly Oat Bars, p 221, ***PointsPlus*** value: ***3***

peppered filet steak with zucchini

serves 4

per serving

- ▲ **4 (115 g [¼-lb]) lean filet mignon steaks, trimmed**
- **15 ml (1 Tbsp) mixed peppercorns, cracked**
- **1 ml (¼ tsp) coarse sea salt**
- **5 ml (1 tsp) canola oil**
- ▲ **2 zucchinis, halved lengthwise and thinly sliced**
- **2 shallots, minced**
- ▲ **125 ml (½ cup) reduced-sodium chicken broth**
- **15 ml (1 Tbsp) Dijon mustard**

1 Sprinkle steaks with cracked pepper and salt, pressing to adhere. Heat oil in large heavy skillet over medium-high heat. Add steaks and cook until bottoms are browned, about 4 minutes. Turn steaks over and cook until instant-read thermometer inserted into centres registers 63°C (145°F) for medium-rare, about 3 minutes. Transfer steaks to plate and cover with foil.

2 Add zucchini and shallots to skillet. Cook, stirring often, until softened, about 3 minutes. Add broth and mustard and stir gently. Simmer until liquid thickens, about 3 minutes. Serve zucchini and sauce with steaks.

Per serving (1 steak and 150 ml [⅔ cup] zucchini and sauce): 212 Cal, 8 g Total Fat, 3 g Sat Fat, 0 g Trans Fat, 67 mg Chol, 332 mg Sod, 7 g Carb, 2 g Sugar, 1 g Fib, 26 g Prot, 41 mg Calc.

peppered filet steak with zucchini

beef and broccoli stir-fry

serves 4

per serving

- Juice of 1 orange
- 30 ml (2 Tbsp) hoisin sauce
- 2 cloves garlic, minced
- Pinch red pepper flakes
- ▲ 340 g (¾ lb) lean thin-sliced top-round steak, trimmed and cut into strips
- 10 ml (2 tsp) Asian (dark) sesame oil
- ▲ 1 L (4 cups) small broccoli florets

1 Combine orange juice, hoisin sauce, garlic, and pepper flakes in large bowl. Add steak and toss to coat.

2 Heat large skillet or wok over medium-high heat until drop of water sizzles on it. Add 5 ml (1 tsp) of oil and swirl to coat pan. Remove steak from marinade (reserve marinade) and add to skillet. Stir-fry until steak is no longer pink, about 2 minutes. Transfer to plate.

3 Heat remaining 5 ml (1 tsp) oil in skillet. Add broccoli and stir-fry until bright green, about 3 minutes. Add steak and reserved marinade. Stir-fry until liquid has evaporated and steak is heated through, about 1 minute.

Per serving (310 ml [1¼ cups]): 188 Cal, 7 g Total Fat, 2 g Sat Fat, 0 g Trans Fat, 49 mg Chol, 176 mg Sod, 10 g Carb, 4 g Sugar, 2 g Fib, 23 g Prot, 46 mg Calc.

thai-style beef salad

serves 4

per serving

- 45 ml (3 Tbsp) seasoned rice vinegar
- 15 ml (1 Tbsp) reduced-sodium soy sauce
- 5 ml (1 tsp) packed brown sugar
- ▲ 454-g (16-oz) bag coleslaw mix
- 60 ml (¼ cup) chopped fresh cilantro
- 60 ml (¼ cup) chopped fresh mint
- ▲ 225 g (½ lb) sliced lean sirloin roast beef, cut into strips
- 30 ml (2 Tbsp) unsalted dry-roasted peanuts

Combine vinegar, soy sauce, and brown sugar in large bowl. Add coleslaw mix, cilantro, and mint; toss to coat. Top with beef and peanuts, and serve.

Per serving (425 ml [1¾ cups]): 148 Cal, 5 g Total Fat, 1 g Sat Fat, 0 g Trans Fat, 25 mg Chol, 405 mg Sod, 11 g Carb, 4 g Sugar, 3 g Fib, 16 g Prot, 70 mg Calc.

stay on track

If you like you can enjoy this savoury no-cook salad as a lettuce wrap by spooning each serving into 3 or 4 large Boston or red leaf lettuce leaves, folding in the tops and bottoms, and rolling the leaves closed.

pork chops with cherry pan sauce

pork chops with cherry pan sauce

serves 4

per serving

- ▲ **4 (140-g [5-oz]) lean boneless centre-cut pork loin chops, trimmed**
- **1 ml (¼ tsp) black pepper**
- **2 ml (½ tsp) salt**
- **10 ml (2 tsp) canola oil**
- ▲ **125 ml (½ cup) reduced-sodium chicken broth**
- **60 ml (¼ cup) no-sugar-added cherry preserves**
- **15 ml (1 Tbsp) grated orange zest**

1 Sprinkle pork chops with pepper and 1 ml (¼ tsp) salt. Heat oil in large skillet over medium-high heat. Add pork to skillet and cook until browned, about 3 minutes per side. Transfer to plate and cover loosely with foil.

2 Add broth to skillet and bring to boil over high heat, scraping up any browned bits from bottom of pan. Stir in cherry preserves, orange zest, and remaining 1 ml (¼ tsp) salt and simmer 1 minute.

3 Return pork and any accumulated juices to skillet; cook just until pork is barely pink in middle and instant-read thermometer inserted into centre of chops registers 63°C (145°F), about 3 minutes.

Per serving (1 pork chop and 30 ml [2 Tbsp] sauce): 255 Cal, 10 g Total Fat, 2 g Sat Fat, 0 g Trans Fat, 83 mg Chol, 355 mg Sod, 14 g Carb, 12 g Sugar, 0 g Fib, 27 g Prot, 27 mg Calc.

stay on track

Steamed broccolini (also known as asparation) and butternut squash purée make healthful and colourful side dishes for this pork.

pesto and pepperoni french bread pizzas

serves 4

per serving

- 1 (225-g [8-oz]) loaf whole wheat French bread, split
- 30 ml (2 Tbsp) prepared pesto
- ▲ 2 plum tomatoes, diced
- ▲ 125 ml (½ cup) shredded fat-free mozzarella cheese
- 12 thin slices pepperoni (55 g [2 oz])
- 30 ml (2 Tbsp) chopped fresh basil

1 Preheat broiler. Line baking sheet with foil.

2 Pull out some of the soft centre from each piece of bread. (Discard or save for bread crumbs.) Place bread halves, cut side up, on prepared pan. Spread 15 ml (1 Tbsp) pesto on each piece. Top each evenly with tomatoes, mozzarella, and pepperoni.

3 Broil pizzas 15 cm (6 in) from heat until topping is hot and cheese is melted, about 6 minutes. Sprinkle each with basil and cut crosswise in half to make a total of 4 pizzas. Serve at once.

Per serving (1 piece pizza): 243 Cal, 8 g Total Fat, 2 g Sat Fat, 0 g Trans Fat, 11 mg Chol, 600 mg Sod, 32 g Carb, 4 g Sugar, 4 g Fib, 13 g Prot, 101 mg Calc.

stay on track

Try serving this pizza with a satisfying Italian-style salad of thinly sliced radicchio, romaine, and endive tossed with balsamic vinegar.

chicken and rice burritos

serves 4

per serving

- ▲ **340 g (¾ lb) thin-sliced skinless boneless chicken breast cutlets, cut into 1.25-cm (½-in) strips**
- **1 ml (¼ tsp) salt**
- **5 ml (1 tsp) canola oil**
- **2 garlic cloves, minced**
- ▲ **250 ml (1 cup) cooked brown rice**
- **4 (20 cm [8-in]) flour tortillas**
- ▲ **125 ml (½ cup) fat-free salsa**
- **60 ml (¼ cup) shredded reduced-fat Mexican cheese blend**

1 Sprinkle chicken with salt. Heat oil in large nonstick skillet over medium-high heat. Add chicken and cook, turning occasionally, until lightly browned, about 6 minutes. Stir in garlic and cook 1 minute. Stir in rice and cook, stirring occasionally, until heated through, about 2 minutes.

2 Meanwhile, warm tortillas according to package directions.

3 Put 1 tortilla on work surface and spoon one-quarter of chicken-and-rice mixture down centre. Top with 30 ml (2 Tbsp) salsa and 15 ml (1 Tbsp) Mexican cheese blend; roll up tortilla. Repeat with remaining tortillas, chicken mixture, salsa, and cheese.

Per serving (1 burrito): 305 Cal, 8 g Total Fat, 2 g Sat Fat, 0 g Trans Fat, 59 mg Chol, 748 mg Sod, 33 g Carb, 3 g Sugar, 2 g Fib, 25 g Prot, 141 mg Calc.

polenta with sausage and peppers

serves 4

per serving

- ▲ 1 450-g (16-oz) tube fat-free polenta, cut into 12 slices
- 5 ml (1 tsp) olive oil
- ▲ 2 bell peppers, sliced
- ▲ 1 onion, sliced
- 225 g (½ lb) cooked Italian-style chicken sausage, thinly sliced
- ▲ 150 ml (⅔ cup) canned no-salt-added tomato sauce
- 60 ml (¼ cup) water
- 6 kalamata olives, pitted and chopped
- 60 ml (¼ cup) lightly packed fresh basil leaves, sliced

1 Preheat broiler. Line baking sheet with foil; spray foil with nonstick spray.

2 Arrange polenta slices in single layer on prepared pan. Spray lightly with nonstick spray. Broil 15 cm (6 in) from heat just until golden, about 3 minutes per side. Keep warm.

3 Meanwhile, heat oil in large nonstick skillet over medium-high heat. Add bell peppers and onion. Cook, stirring often, until softened, about 4 minutes. Stir in sausage; cook until sausage is lightly browned, about 2 minutes.

4 Stir in tomato sauce, water, and olives; bring to boil. Reduce heat and simmer until vegetables are tender, about 1 minute. Serve sauce over polenta and sprinkle with basil.

Per serving (3 slices polenta and 250 ml [1 cup] vegetables and sausage): 258 Cal, 8 g Total Fat, 0 g Sat Fat, 0 g Trans Fat, 43 mg Chol, 885 mg Sod, 33 g Carb, 7 g Sugar, 4 g Fib, 14 g Prot, 209 mg Calc.

for your information

Fully cooked chicken sausages are a great time-saver because they need only a few minutes to heat through. They can vary greatly in fat content—look for brands that contain 5 grams of fat or less per link.

polenta with sausage and peppers

sweet-and-savoury cabbage slaw with smoked chicken

serves 4

4 *PointsPlus®* value per serving

- **30 ml (2 Tbsp) rice vinegar**
- **22 ml (1½ Tbsp) reduced-sodium soy sauce**
- **15 ml (1 Tbsp) grated peeled fresh ginger**
- **10 ml (2 tsp) canola oil**
- **10 ml (2 tsp) honey**
- ▲ **1 L (4 cups) thinly sliced Napa cabbage**
- ▲ **1 large carrot, shredded**
- **250 ml (1 cup) finely chopped smoked chicken breast**
- ▲ **4 scallions, thinly sliced**

Mix vinegar, soy sauce, ginger, oil, and honey together in medium bowl. Add cabbage, carrot, chicken, and scallions; toss to coat.

Per serving (325 ml [1⅓ cups]): 125 Cal, 5 g Total Fat, 1 g Sat Fat, 0 g Trans Fat, 30 mg Chol, 714 mg Sod, 14 g Carb, 6 g Sugar, 3 g Fib, 12 g Prot, 51 mg Calc.

stay on track

Bulk up this light dinner salad with some whole-grain noodles; a 125-ml (½-cup) serving of cooked whole wheat pasta per person will increase the ***PointsPlus*** value by **2**.

barbecue turkey sandwiches

serves 4

per serving

- ▲ **225 g (½ lb) sliced lean low-sodium skinless roast turkey breast, diced**
- **175 ml (¾ cup) low-sodium barbecue sauce**
- **15 ml (1 Tbsp) apple cider vinegar**
- ▲ **4 light whole-grain hamburger buns, split**
- ▲ **250 ml (1 cup) thinly sliced red cabbage**
- ▲ **1 small dill pickle (made without added sugar), cut into 12 slices**

1 Combine turkey, barbecue sauce, and vinegar in medium saucepan. Cover and cook over medium heat, stirring occasionally, until heated through, about 5 minutes.

2 Fill buns with 125 ml (½ cup) turkey mixture, 60 ml (¼ cup) cabbage, and 3 pickle slices. Serve at once.

Per serving (1 sandwich): 262 Cal, 4 g Total Fat, 1 g Sat Fat, 0 g Trans Fat, 30 mg Chol, 847 mg Sod, 47 g Carb, 20 g Sugar, 4 g Fib, 14 g Prot, 64 mg Calc.

turkey scaloppine with asparagus

turkey scaloppine with asparagus

serves 4

per serving

- ▲ **450 g (1 lb) asparagus, trimmed**
- ▲ **570 g (1¼ lb) thin-sliced turkey breast cutlet, cut into 4 pieces**
- **5 ml (1 tsp) paprika**
- **2 ml (½ tsp) salt**
- **1 ml (¼ tsp) black pepper**
- **15 ml (3 tsp) unsalted butter**
- ▲ **75 ml (⅓ cup) reduced-sodium chicken broth**
- **60 ml (¼ cup) dry white wine**
- **45 ml (3 Tbsp) lemon juice**
- **30 ml (2 Tbsp) drained capers**

1 Put asparagus in steamer basket; set in pot over 2.5 cm (1 in) of boiling water. Cover tightly and steam just until tender, 4–6 minutes. Keep warm.

2 Meanwhile, sprinkle turkey pieces with paprika, salt, and pepper. Melt 5ml (1 tsp) butter in nonstick skillet over medium-high heat. Add turkey and cook until lightly browned, about 2 minutes per side. Add broth, wine, lemon juice, and capers; bring to boil. Reduce heat and simmer, uncovered, turning turkey once, until cooked through, about 3 minutes.

3 Remove skillet from heat and swirl in remaining 10 ml (2 tsp) butter. Serve turkey with sauce and asparagus.

Per serving (1 piece turkey, 30 ml (2 Tbsp) sauce, and about 5 asparagus spears): 220 Cal, 4 g Total Fat, 2 g Sat Fat, 0 g Trans Fat, 64 mg Chol, 553 mg Sod, 7 g Carb, 2 g Sugar, 3 g Fib, 38 g Prot, 33 mg Calc.

stay on track

A serving of a quick-cooking whole grain is a great side with this dish; a 125-ml (½-cup) serving of either cooked whole wheat couscous or quinoa will increase the per-serving ***PointsPlus*** value by **3**.

grilled sea bass with chili-lime butter

serves 4

per serving

- **30 ml (2 Tbsp) unsalted butter, softened**
- **15 ml (1 Tbsp) finely chopped fresh cilantro**
- **10 ml (2 tsp) grated lime zest**
- **5 ml (1 tsp) chili powder**
- **2 ml (½ tsp) salt**
- ▲ **4 (170-g [6-oz]) pieces skin-on sea bass fillet**
- **5 ml (1 tsp) canola oil**
- **5 ml (1 tsp) ground cumin**

1 Spray grill rack with nonstick spray. Prepare grill.

2 Combine butter, cilantro, lime zest, chili powder, and 1 ml (¼ tsp) salt in small bowl and mash with back of spoon until combined; set aside.

3 Brush sea bass fillets on all sides with oil and sprinkle with cumin and remaining 1 ml (¼ tsp) salt. Place on grill rack and cook until browned and just opaque in centre, 3–4 minutes per side. Remove and discard skin and top each fillet with chili-lime butter.

Per serving (1 fillet and 10 ml (2 tsp) chili-lime butter): 239 Cal, 11 g Total Fat, 5 g Sat Fat, 0 g Trans Fat, 89 mg Chol, 420 mg Sod, 1 g Carb, 0 g Sugar, 1 g Fib, 33 g Prot, 27 mg Calc.

for your information

The skin on the fillets will help them stay intact and flip more easily for grilling. You can remove it after cooking.

tuna teriyaki with ginger bok choy

serves 4

per serving

- ▲ **4 (170-g [6-oz]) tuna steaks, about 2.5 cm (1 in) thick**
- **30 ml (2 Tbsp) teriyaki sauce**
- **30 ml (2 Tbsp) lemon juice**
- **15 ml (1 Tbsp) reduced-sodium soy sauce**
- **15 ml (1 Tbsp) grated peeled fresh ginger**
- **10 ml (2 tsp) Asian (dark) sesame oil**
- **Pinch red pepper flakes**
- ▲ **4 baby bok choy, each split lengthwise**

1 Place tuna in large zip-close plastic bag; add teriyaki sauce. Squeeze out air and seal bag; turn to coat tuna. Let marinate while preparing bok choy.

2 Heat ridged grill pan over high heat. Combine lemon juice, soy sauce, ginger, oil, and pepper flakes in large bowl. Add bok choy and toss to coat. Place on grill pan and grill just until tender, 3–4 minutes per side. Transfer to platter and cover.

3 Remove tuna from marinade. Discard marinade. Add tuna to pan and grill over high heat until browned and just pink in centre, 2–3 minutes per side. Serve with bok choy.

Per serving (1 tuna steak and 2 pieces bok choy): 275 Cal, 10 g Total Fat, 2 g Sat Fat, 0 g Trans Fat, 63 mg Chol, 566 mg Sod, 4 g Carb, 2 g Sugar, 1 g Fib, 40 g Prot, 17 mg Calc.

balinese salmon salad

serves 4

per serving

- ▲ 2 (170-g [6-oz]) cans wild sockeye salmon, drained
- ▲ 1 (340-g [¾-lb]) ripe papaya, peeled, seeded, and cut into 5-cm (2-in) thick strips
- ▲ 1 Kirby (pickling) cucumber, halved lengthwise and thinly sliced
- ▲ 250 ml (1 cup) mung bean sprouts
- 1 large shallot, peeled, halved, and very thinly sliced
- ▲ 1 small Thai chile pepper, seeded and minced
- Juice of 1 lime
- 10 ml (2 tsp) Asian fish sauce
- 60 ml (¼ cup) chopped fresh basil leaves
- 30 ml (2 Tbsp) chopped unsalted dry-roasted peanuts

1 Place salmon in large bowl; pick out and discard any bones or large pieces of skin. Gently break salmon into chunks with fork.

2 Add papaya, cucumber, bean sprouts, shallot, chile pepper, lime juice, and fish sauce to bowl and toss to combine. Add basil and toss again. Serve garnished with peanuts.

Per serving (310 ml [1¼ cups]) salmon salad and 7 ml [½ Tbsp] peanuts): 224 Cal, 12 g Total Fat, 2 g Sat Fat, 0 g Trans Fat, 54 mg Chol, 603 mg Sod, 12 g Carb, 6 g Sugar, 2 g Fib, 21 g Prot, 172 mg Calc.

for your information

Wild salmon is generally lower in fat and higher in heart-healthy omega-3 fatty acids than farm-raised salmon.

grilled shrimp caesar salad

serves 4

per serving

- ▲ **680 g (1½ lb) extra-large peeled and deveined shrimp**
- **10 ml (2 tsp) Cajun seasoning**
- ▲ **1 (340-g [12-oz]) bag chopped romaine lettuce**
- **60 ml (¼ cup) reduced-fat Caesar dressing**
- **30 ml (2 Tbsp) grated Parmesan cheese**
- **1 ml (¼ tsp) black pepper**

1 Sprinkle shrimp with Cajun seasoning. Heat ridged grill pan over medium-high heat. Place half of shrimp on pan and grill until lightly browned and just opaque in centre, about 2 minutes per side. Transfer to plate. Repeat with remaining shrimp.

2 Meanwhile, toss together lettuce and dressing in large bowl. Divide among 4 plates and sprinkle evenly with Parmesan and pepper. Top with shrimp and serve at once.

Per serving (about 7 shrimp, 750 ml [3 cups] salad, and 7 ml [½ Tbsp] cheese): 170 Cal, 3 g Total Fat, 1 g Sat Fat, 0 g Trans Fat, 255 mg Chol, 766 mg Sod, 6 g Carb, 3 g Sugar, 2 g Fib, 29 g Prot, 110 mg Calc.

hoisin mushrooms and tofu

serves 4

per serving

- **10 ml (2 tsp) Asian (dark) sesame oil**
- ▲ **390 g (14 oz) firm tofu, drained and cubed**
- ▲ **225 g (8 oz) sliced shiitake mushrooms**
- ▲ **1 bunch scallions, sliced**
- **60 ml (¼cup) hoisin sauce**
- **30 ml (2 Tbsp) water**

1 Heat large skillet or wok over medium-high heat until drop of water sizzles on it. Add 5 ml (1 tsp) of oil and swirl to coat skillet. Add tofu and stir-fry until lightly golden, 4–5 minutes. Transfer to bowl.

2 Heat remaining 5 ml (1 tsp) oil in skillet. Add mushrooms and stir-fry until tender, 4–5 minutes. Add scallions and stir-fry just until wilted, about 30 seconds. Add hoisin sauce, water, and tofu. Cook, stirring constantly, until tofu is heated through, about 2 minutes.

Per serving (175 ml [¾ cup]): 189 Cal, 8 g Total Fat, 1 g Sat Fat, 0 g Trans Fat, 0 mg Chol, 268 mg Sod, 21 g Carb, 7 g Sugar, 3 g Fib, 11 g Prot, 228 mg Calc.

stay on track

Change things up a bit by serving this savoury stir-fry over nutty, quick-cooking bulgur instead of the usual rice; a 125-ml (½-cup) portion of cooked bulgur per person will increase the ***PointsPlus*** value by **2**.

portobello cheeseburgers with pesto mayonnaise

serves 4

per serving

- ▲ **4 (85-g [3-oz]) portobello mushroom caps**
- **15 ml (1 Tbsp) reduced-fat balsamic dressing**
- **1 ml (¼ tsp) salt**
- **1 ml (¼ tsp) black pepper**
- ▲ **4 (21-g [¾-oz]) slices low fat Muenster cheese**
- **30 ml (2 Tbsp) fat-free mayonnaise**
- **15 ml (1 Tbsp) prepared pesto**
- ▲ **4 light multigrain English muffins, split and toasted**

1 Heat ridged grill pan over medium-high heat.

2 Brush mushrooms all over with dressing; sprinkle with salt and pepper. Place mushrooms, round side up, on pan and grill until they begin to release their liquid, about 4 minutes. Turn and cook, round side down, until almost tender, about 2 minutes. Top each mushroom with 1 slice Muenster cheese; cook until cheese is melted and mushrooms are tender, 1–2 minutes longer.

3 Meanwhile, combine mayonnaise and pesto in small bowl. Spread mixture evenly on cut sides of muffins. Fill each muffin with 1 mushroom and serve at once.

Per serving (1 filled sandwich): 245 Cal, 8 g Total Fat, 3 g Sat Fat, 0 g Trans Fat, 15 mg Chol, 635 mg Sod, 33 g Carb, 9 g Sugar, 6 g Fib, 13 g Prot, 300 mg Calc

YOUR SECOND MONTH

—

Ready in 20 Minutes or Less

breakfasts

Farmer's Frittata with Goat Cheese
Easy Huevo Ranchero
Berries-and-Cream French Toast
Buckwheat Pancakes with Bananas
Baked Oatmeal Brûlée
Tropical Breakfast Parfait

lunches

Turkey and Prosciutto Italian Hero
Spicy Vietnamese Chicken Wraps
Tuna-and-Dill Baguette Sandwiches with Tomato Salad
Beef and Vegetable Borscht
Pork and Soba Noodle Soup
Vegetarian Chili Soup
Classic Steak and Blue Cheese Salad
Couscous Salad with Smoked Turkey and Apples
Spinach Salad with Grilled Chicken and Raspberries
Shrimp, Orange, and Fennel Chopped Salad
Greek Barley Salad
Tortellini Salad with Tomatoes and Broccoli
Provençal Stuffed Tomatoes

dinners

Apricot-Glazed Steak Kebabs
Grilled Bison Sliders
Spicy Pork and Pineapple Skewers
Duck with Red Wine and Rosemary
Grilled Chicken with Tropical Salsa
Ultimate Turkey Burgers
Peppered Tuna Steak with Artichokes
Salmon Cakes with Dijon-Herb Sauce
Shrimp and Asparagus Frittata
Easy Scampi with Edamame
Curried Rice Noodles with Seafood
Mussels Marinara
Udon and Scallops in Miso-Ginger Broth
Tofu and Vegetables in Coconut Sauce
Spaghetti with Feta and Walnuts
Pear and Roquefort Pizza

farmer's frittata with goat cheese

serves 2

per serving

- 5 ml (1 tsp) olive oil
- ▲ 1 small (115-g [4-oz]) red potato, shredded
- ▲ 1 small zucchini, diced
- ▲ 60 ml (¼ cup) diced onion
- ▲ 60 ml (¼ cup)diced bell pepper
- Pinch salt
- 0.5 ml (⅛ tsp) black pepper
- 15 ml (1 Tbsp) sliced fresh basil, plus more for garnish
- ▲ 1 large egg
- ▲ 4 large egg whites
- 75 ml (⅓ cup) crumbled soft goat cheese

1 Heat oil in medium nonstick skillet over medium-high heat. Add potato, zucchini, onion, bell pepper, salt, and black pepper. Cook, stirring frequently, until vegetables are tender, about 4 minutes. Stir in 15 ml (1 Tbsp) of basil.

2 Meanwhile, beat egg and egg whites in medium bowl until frothy. Pour eggs over vegetables and reduce heat to medium. Cook, lifting edges frequently with spatula to let uncooked egg flow underneath, until eggs are almost set, 2–3 minutes.

3 Sprinkle goat cheese over frittata. Cover skillet and reduce heat to low. Cook until cheese melts slightly, about 2 minutes. Cut frittata in half and slide each half onto plate. Sprinkle with remaining basil.

Per serving **(½ frittata): 206 Cal, 9 g Total Fat, 4 g Sat Fat, 0 g Trans Fat, 117 mg Chol, 304 mg Sod, 15 g Carb, 4 g Sugar, 2 g Fib, 16 g Prot, 72 mg Calc.**

stay on track

Filling veggies and lots of protein make this a great dish for anytime of the day, not just breakfast. You can even serve it warm or at room temperature as a sandwich filling; use 2 slices of reduced-calorie whole wheat bread for each sandwich, and increase the ***PointsPlus*** value by **3**.

farmer's frittata with goat cheese

easy huevo ranchero

serves 1

per serving

- ▲ 45 ml (3 Tbsp) canned fat-free refried beans
- 1 (15-cm [6-in]) corn tortilla
- 2 ml (½ tsp) canola oil
- ▲ 1 large egg
- ▲ 30 ml (2 Tbsp) fat-free salsa, at room temperature
- ▲ 10 ml (2 tsp) fat-free sour cream
- 15 ml (1 Tbsp) chopped fresh cilantro

1 Place refried beans in small microwavable bowl. Microwave on High until very hot, 45–60 seconds, stopping to stir every 15 seconds. Keep warm. Place tortilla on plate and cover with paper towel. Microwave until warm, 20–30 seconds. Keep warm.

2 Heat oil in small skillet over medium heat. Beat egg in small bowl until frothy; pour into skillet and cook, stirring, just until set, about 3 minutes.

3 Spread tortilla with beans. Top with egg, salsa, sour cream, and cilantro.

Per serving **(1 filled tortilla): 216 Cal, 8 g Total Fat, 2 g Sat Fat, 0 g Trans Fat, 216 mg Chol, 447 mg Sod, 26 g Carb, 2 g Sugar, 3 g Fib, 9 g Prot, 39 mg Calc.**

berries-and-cream french toast

serves 2

per serving

30 ml (2 Tbsp) fat-free cream cheese

4 slices cinnamon-raisin bread

▲ 250 ml (1 cup) thinly sliced hulled strawberries

▲ 75 ml (⅓ cup) light (5% M.F.) cream

▲ 1 large egg

Few drops almond extract

5 ml (1 tsp) canola oil

1 Spread cream cheese evenly on one side of each slice of bread. Top each of 2 slices of bread with 60 ml (¼ cup) strawberries and cover with remaining slices.

2 Combine cream, egg, and almond extract in small shallow bowl and beat until frothy.

3 Heat oil in large nonstick skillet over medium heat. Dip sandwiches, one at a time, into egg mixture. Place sandwiches in skillet and cook until golden brown, 3–4 minutes per side. Cut sandwiches in half on diagonal and top with remaining strawberries.

Per serving (2 stuffed halves and 60 ml [¼ cup] berries): 337 Cal, 10 g Total Fat, 3 g Sat Fat, 0 g Trans Fat, 118 mg Chol, 427 mg Sod, 45 g Carb, 23 g Sugar, 3 g Fib, 13 g Prot, 130 mg Calc.

stay on track

Fresh fruit is a colourful and refreshing topping for pancakes and French toast and has the added benefit of helping you feel full and satisfied long after breakfast is over.

buckwheat pancakes with bananas

buckwheat pancakes with bananas

serves 4

per serving

- ▲ **1 large egg**
- ▲ **1 large egg white**
- **250 ml (1 cup) low-fat buttermilk**
- ▲ **125 ml (½ cup) mashed ripe banana**
- **10 ml (2 tsp) honey**
- **125 ml (½ cup) + 30 ml (2 Tbsp) all-purpose flour**
- **125 ml (½ cup) buckwheat flour**
- **10 ml (2 tsp) baking powder**
- **1 ml (¼ tsp) salt**
- **10 ml (2 tsp) canola oil**
- ▲ **500 ml (2 cups) sliced bananas**

1 Combine egg, egg white, buttermilk, mashed banana, and honey in large bowl. Combine all-purpose flour, buckwheat flour, baking powder, and salt in medium bowl. Stir flour mixture into buttermilk mixture just until blended.

2 Heat 5 ml (1 tsp) oil on nonstick griddle or in large nonstick skillet over medium-low heat. Pour batter by 60-ml (¼-cup) measures onto griddle. Cook just until bubbles begin to appear at edges of pancakes, about 3 minutes. Flip and cook about 2 minutes longer. Repeat with remaining batter and oil to make a total of 12 pancakes. Top pancakes with sliced bananas.

Per serving **(3 pancakes and 125 ml [½ cup] sliced banana): 296 Cal, 5 g Total Fat, 1 g Sat Fat, 0 g Trans Fat, 56 mg Chol, 518 mg Sod, 57 g Carb, 19 g Sugar, 5 g Fib, 9 g Prot, 140 mg Calc.**

for your information

These pancakes will keep refrigerated up to 2 days, or freeze them individually wrapped up to 3 months. Reheat pancakes in the microwave or in a 150°C (300°F) oven.

baked oatmeal brûlée

serves 6

per serving

- ▲ **1 L (4 cups) skim milk**
- ▲ **750 ml (3 cups) old-fashioned rolled oats**
- **75 ml (1/3 cup) raisins, chopped**
- **2 ml (1/2 tsp) ground ginger**
- **2 ml (1/2 tsp) cinnamon**
- **1 ml (1/4 tsp) grated nutmeg**
- **1 ml (1/4 tsp) salt**
- **22 ml (1 1/2 Tbsp) packed brown sugar**

1 Preheat broiler. Bring milk to simmer in large saucepan over medium-high heat.

2 Stir oats and raisins into hot milk. Cook, stirring frequently, 2 minutes. Stir in ginger, cinnamon, nutmeg, and salt. Reduce heat to medium-low and cook until mixture is creamy, about 3 minutes.

3 Spread cooked cereal into 20-cm (8-in) square baking dish. Sprinkle brown sugar evenly over top; broil 12.5 cm (5 in) from heat until sugar caramelizes, about 1 minute. Let stand at room temperature about 2 minutes. Cut into 6 servings.

Per serving **(125 ml [1/2 cup]): 249 Cal, 3 g Total Fat, 1 g Sat Fat, 0 g Trans Fat, 3 mg Chol, 169 mg Sod, 46 g Carb, 19 g Sugar, 5 g Fib, 11 g Prot, 214 mg Calc.**

stay on track

This is a terrific breakfast to make up over the weekend and enjoy throughout the week as healthful, microwave-quick breakfasts. It will keep refrigerated for 5 days, or you can freeze individual portions.

tropical breakfast parfait

serves 1

per serving

- ▲ **125 ml (½ cup) finely diced pineapple**
- ▲ **1 kiwifruit, peeled and diced**
- **5 ml (1 tsp) lime juice**
- **1 ml (¼ tsp) sugar**
- ▲ **250 ml (1 cup) plain fat-free yogourt**
- **15 ml (1 Tbsp) reduced-fat granola**
- **15 ml (1 Tbsp) unsweetened shredded coconut, toasted**

1 Stir together pineapple, kiwifruit, lime juice, and sugar in medium bowl. Let stand 10 minutes.

2 Spoon half of fruit and juice into parfait glass; top with 125 ml (½ cup) yogourt. Repeat layering. Sprinkle parfait with granola and coconut.

Per serving (1 parfait): 292 Cal, 5 g Total Fat, 4 g Sat Fat, 0 g Trans Fat, 5 mg Chol, 207 mg Sod, 48 g Carb, 37 g Sugar, 5 g Fib, 16 g Prot, 527 mg Calc.

Weekend Indulgences

You ***can*** eat that! If you budget special indulgences into your weekly ***PointsPlus*** Allowance, you can treat yourself to all the foods you love. Try a few of our suggestions this weekend.

Breakfasts

• Enjoy a leisurely morning with our**Buckwheat Pancakes with Bananas**, page 73, and top each serving with 15 ml (1 Tbsp) of pure maple syrup for an extra ***PointsPlus*** value of ***1***.

• Hankering for a biscuit? Stop by the drive-through for a treat on your way to do Saturday morning errands. One fast-food egg biscuit (140 g [5 oz]) has a ***PointsPlus*** value of ***9***.

• Love to have a bagel with cream cheese while you read the Sunday papers (online or off)? Have a small bagel (55 g [2 oz]) spread with 15 ml (1 Tbsp) of cream cheese for a ***PointsPlus*** value of ***7***.

• Gotta have your weekend donut fix? Indulge in a glazed donut (55 g [2 oz]) for a ***PointsPlus*** value of **7** or a jelly-filled donut (85 g [3 oz]) for a ***PointsPlus*** value of ***8***.

Lunches

• Go ahead and have a gooey grilled cheese sandwich when you make them for your kids on the weekend. A grilled cheese sandwich made with 2 slices of whole wheat bread, 2 slices American cheese, and 5 ml (1 tsp) of butter has a ***PointsPlus*** value of ***8***.

• Do you dream of a burger and fries all week? Get your fix with a small fast-food hamburger (85 g [3 oz]) for a ***PointsPlus*** value of **7** and a small order of French fries (70 g [2½ oz]) for a ***PointsPlus*** value of ***6***.

• Turn our **Pepper Jack Quesadillas with Shrimp and Spinach**, page 143, into a fiesta by serving them with a side of guacamole (60 ml [¼ cup] of guacamole per person has a ***PointsPlus*** value of **2**).

• You've had a light breakfast and a veggie-packed soup for lunch. Why not treat yourself to a piece of our **Five-Spice Carrot Cake**, page 204, for dessert? One square has a ***PointsPlus*** value of ***5***.

Dinners

• Serve our extravagant **Wild Salmon en Papillote**, page 174, with chardonnay or pinot grigio. A 150-ml (5-fl oz) glass of white wine has a ***PointsPlus*** value of ***4***.

• Craving steak and a "bake"? Enjoy a baked potato with butter and sour cream alongside our **Peppered Filet Steak with Zucchini**, page 46. A medium baked potato topped with 15 ml (1 Tbsp) butter and 15 ml (1 Tbsp) sour cream adds a ***PointsPlus*** value of ***7*** to the meal.

• Going out for pizza is as easy as... pie! Enjoy a large slice of thin-crust cheese pizza (85 g [3 oz]) for a ***PointsPlus*** value of ***5***.

• If you look forward to Saturday night at your local Tex-Mex restaurant, you don't have to say no to a cocktail. Enjoy a 125-ml (4-fl oz) margarita for a ***PointsPlus*** value of ***9*** or a 125-ml (4-fl oz) glass of sangria for a ***PointsPlus*** value of ***3***.

Snacks

• Our chips with **Black Bean–Queso Dip**, page 193, just begs a cold glass of beer. One 375-ml (12-fl oz) bottle of regular beer adds a ***PointsPlus*** value of ***5***, or you can opt for light beer for a ***PointsPlus*** value of ***3***.

• Take the kids out on a hot summer afternoon for an ice-cream treat—and have one yourself. A small scoop of regular ice cream (125 ml [½ cup]) in a small sugar cone (10 g [⅓ oz]) has a ***PointsPlus*** value of ***5***.

• Warm up on a winter afternoon with a cup of hot cocoa made with 250 ml (1 cup) skim milk, 15 ml (1 Tbsp) unsweetened cocoa, and 15 ml (1 Tbsp) sugar for a ***PointsPlus*** value of ***4***.

Special Times with Friends and Family

• Attending a wedding or a birthday party this weekend? You've gotta have cake! One small slice of cake (55 g [2 oz]) with icing has a ***PointsPlus*** value of ***6***.

• Going to the game? Treat yourself to one of these options for a ***PointsPlus*** value of ***5***: 1 plain 115-g (4-oz) hot dog, 1.3 L (5 cups) light butter-flavoured popcorn, 1 serving of cotton candy (43 g [1½ oz]), or 40 shelled peanuts (30 g [1 oz]).

• Kick off a special night out with a champagne toast. A 125-ml (4-fl oz) glass of champagne has a ***PointsPlus*** value of ***3***.

turkey and prosciutto italian hero

serves 1

per serving

- ▲ **15 ml (1 Tbsp) finely chopped red onion**
- **3 small black olives (not cured in oil), pitted and chopped**
- **4 chopped fresh basil leaves**
- **2 ml (½ tsp) red-wine vinegar**
- **2 ml (½ tsp) olive oil**
- **1 small (10-cm [4-in]) crusty whole wheat submarine roll, split**
- ▲ **1 (21-g [¾-oz]) slice lean skinless low-sodium roast turkey breast**
- **1 (7-g [¼-oz]) slice prosciutto**
- ▲ **½ roasted red bell pepper (not packed in oil), cut into strips**

Combine onion, olives, basil, vinegar, and oil in small bowl. Pull out soft centre from roll. (Discard bread or save for bread crumbs.) Spread onion mixture on bottom half of roll; layer with turkey, prosciutto, and bell pepper. Close sandwich and cut in half.

Per serving (1 sandwich): 256 Cal, 8 g Total Fat, 2 g Sat Fat, 0 g Trans Fat, 17 mg Chol, 870 mg Sod, 38 g Carb, 7 g Sugar, 6 g Fib, 12 g Prot, 86 mg Calc.

stay on track

Get into the habit of eating some fruit or veggies with your lunchtime sandwich. For this one try a quick slaw of shredded zucchini and carrot tossed with balsamic vinegar and a pinch each of salt and pepper.

spicy vietnamese chicken wraps

serves 2

per serving

- 10 ml (2 tsp) rice vinegar
- 10 ml (2 tsp) reduced-sodium soy sauce
- 2 ml (½ tsp) Sriracha or other hot sauce, or to taste
- ▲ 1 carrot, shredded
- ▲ 3 scallions, sliced
- 30 ml (2 Tbsp) chopped fresh cilantro
- 2 ml (½ tsp) canola oil
- 1 garlic clove, minced
- ▲ 250 ml (1 cup) (115 g [¼ lb]) finely chopped cooked skinless chicken breast
- 1 (25-cm [10-in]) flour tortilla, warmed
- 15 ml (1 Tbsp) fat-free mayonnaise

1 Whisk vinegar, soy sauce, and Sriracha together in small bowl. Add carrot, scallions, and cilantro; toss to coat.

2 Heat oil in medium nonstick skillet over medium-high heat. Add garlic and cook, stirring, until fragrant, about 1 minute. Add chicken and cook, stirring frequently, until heated through, about 3 minutes.

3 Spread tortilla with mayonnaise. Spoon carrot and chicken mixtures over tortilla and roll up. Cut in half.

Per serving (½ wrap): 242 Cal, 5 g Total Fat, 1 g Sat Fat, 0 g Trans Fat, 60 mg Chol, 582 mg Sod, 24 g Carb, 3 g Sugar, 3 g Fib, 26 g Prot, 62 mg Calc.

tuna-and-dill baguette sandwiches with tomato salad

serves 2

per serving

- ▲ **1 (170-g [6-oz]) can low-sodium water-packed tuna, drained**
- ▲ **125 ml (½ cup) diced celery**
- **60 ml (¼ cup) chopped fresh dill**
- **37 ml (2 ½ Tbsp) fat-free mayonnaise**
- ▲ **30 ml (2 Tbsp) chopped red onion**
- **15 ml (1 Tbsp) capers, drained and chopped**
- **10 ml (2 tsp) lemon juice**
- **Black pepper to taste**
- **½ (225-g [8-oz]) whole wheat baguette**
- ▲ **500 ml (2 cups) small tomatoes (cherry, grape, or cocktail or a mix of types), halved**
- **10 ml (2 tsp) red-wine vinegar**

1 Combine tuna, celery, dill, mayonnaise, onion, capers, lemon juice, and pepper in small bowl and mash with fork until blended.

2 Slice baguette lengthwise almost all the way through. Pull out soft centre from both halves, leaving 1.25-cm (½-in) thick shell. (Discard bread or save for bread crumbs.) Spoon tuna mixture into baguette. Close baguette and cut into 2 sandwiches.

3 Toss tomatoes and vinegar together in small bowl; season with pepper to taste. Serve with sandwiches.

Per serving **(1 sandwich and 250 ml [1 cup] tomatoes): 251 Cal, 3 g Total Fat, 0 g Sat Fat, 0 g Trans Fat, 23 mg Chol, 580 mg Sod, 33 g Carb, 9 g Sugar, 5 g Fib, 24 g Prot, 41 mg Calc.**

for your information

If it's summertime, you may want to replace dill in this recipe with chopped fresh basil at its flavourful best.

tuna-and-dill baguette sandwiches
with tomato salad

beef and vegetable borscht

serves 4

per serving

- ▲ **1 (414-ml [14¼-fl oz]) can no-salt-added diced tomatoes with juice**
- ▲ **450-ml (15-fl oz) reduced-sodium beef broth**
- **1 (450-g [16-oz]) jar pickled beets, drained and liquid reserved**
- ▲ **625 ml (2½ cups) sliced green cabbage**
- ▲ **1 carrot, grated**
- ▲ **4 scallions, chopped**
- ▲ **115 g (¼ lb) sliced lean sirloin roast beef, chopped**
- **60 ml (¼ cup) chopped fresh dill**

1 Combine tomatoes, broth, beet liquid, cabbage, carrot, and scallions in medium saucepan; bring to simmer over medium heat. Cook, stirring occasionally, until cabbage and carrot are tender, about 10 minutes.

2 Chop beets and add them to pan; then add beef. Cook, stirring occasionally, until beets and beef are heated through, about 3 minutes. Stir in dill.

Per serving (375 ml [1½ cups]): 185 Cal, 3 g Total Fat, 1 g Sat Fat, 0 g Trans Fat, 16 mg Chol, 154 mg Sod, 27 g Carb, 19 g Sugar, 5 g Fib, 14 g Prot, 78 mg Calc.

stay on track

Enjoy your soup with a slice of toasted reduced-calorie whole wheat bread spread with 5 ml (1 tsp) of Dijon mustard and sprinkled with a few capers; it will help keep you filled up all afternoon and clocks in at a mere ***PointsPlus*** value of ***1***. Leftover soup will keep for 4 days refrigerated.

pork and soba noodle soup

serves 2

per serving

- ▲ **55 g (2 oz) 100% buckwheat soba noodles**
- ▲ **500 ml (2 cups) reduced-sodium chicken broth**
- ▲ **2 baby bok choy, coarsely chopped**
- ▲ **115 g (1/4 lb) lean pork tenderloin, trimmed and thinly sliced**
- **15 ml (1 Tbsp) reduced-sodium soy sauce**
- **7 ml (1 1/2 tsp) minced peeled fresh ginger**
- **1 garlic clove, finely chopped**
- **2 ml (1/2 tsp) Asian (dark) sesame oil**

1 Cook soba noodles according to package directions, omitting salt. Drain.

2 Meanwhile, combine broth, bok choy, pork, soy sauce, ginger, and garlic in large saucepan; bring to simmer over high heat. Reduce heat and simmer until pork is cooked through and bok choy is tender, about 10 minutes.

3 Stir in noodles and ladle into 2 bowls. Drizzle with oil and serve.

Per serving (425 ml [1 3/4 cups] soup and 1 ml [1/4 tsp] sesame oil): 231 Cal, 4 g Total Fat, 1 g Sat Fat, 0 g Trans Fat, 37 mg Chol, 418 mg Sod, 28 g Carb, 3 g Sugar, 3 g Fib, 22 g Prot, 22 mg Calc.

vegetarian chili soup

serves 4

per serving

- 10 ml (2 tsp) canola oil
- ▲ 1 zucchini, diced
- ▲ 5 scallions, thinly sliced
- ▲ 840 ml (28 fl. oz) reduced-sodium vegetable broth
- ▲ 1 (398 ml [14 fl. oz]) can no-salt-added pinto beans, rinsed and drained
- ▲ 250 ml (1 cup) frozen corn kernels
- ▲ 125 ml (1/2 cup) fat-free salsa
- 60 ml (1/4 cup) chopped fresh cilantro

1 Heat oil in large saucepan over medium-high heat. Add zucchini and scallions. Cook, stirring frequently, until vegetables soften, about 3 minutes.

2 Add broth, beans, corn, and salsa; bring to boil. Reduce heat and simmer until flavors blend, about 3 minutes. Divide evenly among 4 bowls and sprinkle with cilantro.

Per serving (425 ml (1 3/4 cups): 179 Cal, 3 g Total Fat, 0 g Sat Fat, 0 g Trans Fat, 0 mg Chol, 250 mg Sod, 31 g Carb, 4 g Sugar, 7 g Fib, 7 g Prot, 88 mg Calc.

for your information

This soup may be refrigerated up to 4 days, ready to be reheated for a quick lunch or light dinner.

classic steak and blue cheese salad

serves 2

per serving

- ▲ **1 (170-g [6-oz]) piece lean flank steak, trimmed**
- **0.5 ml (1/8 tsp) black pepper**
- ▲ **225 g (8 oz) mixed salad greens**
- ▲ **250 ml (1 cup) grape tomatoes, quartered**
- ▲ **1/4 small red onion, thinly sliced**
- **60 ml (1/4 cup) fat-free balsamic dressing**
- **60 ml (1/4 cup) crumbled reduced-fat blue cheese**

1 Spray broiler rack with nonstick spray; preheat broiler.

2 Sprinkle steak with pepper. Place steak on broiler rack and broil 12.5 cm (5 in) from heat until browned and instant-read thermometer inserted in centre registers 63°C (145°F) for medium-rare, 2–3 minutes per side. Transfer to cutting board and let stand 5 minutes.

3 Combine salad greens, tomatoes, and onion in large bowl and toss. Add dressing and blue cheese and toss to coat. Divide between 2 plates. Cut steak thinly against grain into 8 slices; divide evenly and top lettuce with steak. Serve at once.

Per serving **(625 ml [2½ cups] salad with 4 slices steak): 236 Cal, 8 g Total Fat, 4 g Sat Fat, 0 g Trans Fat, 41 mg Chol, 510 mg Sod, 19 g Carb, 11 g Sugar, 4 g Fib, 24 g Prot, 122 mg Calc.**

couscous salad with smoked turkey and apples

couscous salad with smoked turkey and apples

serves 2

8 PointsPlus® value per serving

- 175 ml (3/4 cup) water
- 2 ml (1/2 tsp) curry powder
- 0.5 ml (1/8 tsp) salt
- ▲ 125 ml (1/2 cup) whole wheat couscous
- ▲ 250 ml (1 cup) canned no-salt-added chickpeas, rinsed and drained
- ▲ 1 small apple, cored and diced
- ▲ 125 ml (1/2 cup) (55 g [2 oz]) diced lean low-sodium smoked skinless turkey breast
- ▲ 2 scallions, sliced
- 15 ml (1 Tbsp) lemon juice
- 10 ml (2 tsp) flaxseed or canola oil
- ▲ 750 ml (3 cups) baby spinach leaves

1 Bring water, 1 ml (1/4 tsp) curry powder, and salt to boil in small saucepan. Stir in couscous; cover and remove from heat. Let stand 5 minutes; fluff with fork.

2 Combine chickpeas, apple, turkey, scallions, lemon juice, oil, and remaining 1 ml (1/4 tsp) curry powder in large bowl. Add couscous and toss to combine. Divide spinach between 2 plates and top each portion evenly with couscous and turkey mixture.

Per serving (375 ml [1 1/2 cup] couscous salad and 375 ml [1 1/2 cup] spinach): 339 Cal, 3 g Total Fat, 0 g Sat Fat, 0 g Trans Fat, 13 mg Chol, 487 mg Sod, 65 g Carb, 10 g Sugar, 14 g Fib, 18 g Prot, 107 mg Calc.

stay on track

Adding 2 thinly sliced celery stalks and 1 shredded carrot along with the scallions will give you added crunch and more filling veggies.

spinach salad with grilled chicken and raspberries

serves 2

per serving

- ▲ **2 (115-g [1/4-lb]) thin-sliced skinless boneless chicken cutlets**
- **0.5 ml (1/8 tsp) salt**
- **0.5 ml (1/8 tsp) black pepper**
- ▲ **1 (142-g [4.75-oz]) bag baby spinach**
- ▲ **175 ml (3/4 cup) raspberries**
- ▲ **1 Kirby (pickling) cucumber, thinly sliced**
- ▲ **60 ml (1/4 cup) thinly sliced red onion**
- **75 ml (1/3 cup) fat-free raspberry vinaigrette**

1 Sprinkle chicken with salt and pepper. Spray ridged grill pan with nonstick spray and place over medium-high heat. Place chicken in pan and grill until browned and cooked through, about 4 minutes per side.

2 Meanwhile, combine spinach, raspberries, cucumber, and onion in large bowl. Drizzle with vinaigrette and toss to coat. Divide between 2 plates.

3 Transfer grilled chicken to cutting board and thinly slice. Top each salad with 1 sliced cutlet.

Per serving (750 ml [3 cups] salad and 1 chicken cutlet): 240 Cal, 3 g Total Fat, 1 g Sat Fat, 0 g Trans Fat, 63 mg Chol, 362 mg Sod, 27 g Carb, 11 g Sugar, 7 g Fib, 26 g Prot, 91 mg Calc.

shrimp, orange, and fennel chopped salad

serves 2

per serving

- **10 ml (2 tsp) olive oil**
- **10 ml (2 tsp) apple cider vinegar**
- **5 ml (1 tsp) grated orange zest**
- **2 ml (½ tsp) Dijon mustard**
- **0.5 ml (⅛ tsp) salt**
- ▲ **225 g (½ lb) medium peeled and deveined cooked shrimp**
- ▲ **1 heart of romaine lettuce, chopped**
- ▲ **1 small fennel bulb, diced**
- ▲ **1 navel orange, peeled and chopped**
- ▲ **¼ small red onion, chopped**

Whisk together oil, vinegar, orange zest, mustard, and salt in medium bowl. Add shrimp, lettuce, fennel, orange, and onion and toss to coat. Divide between 2 plates.

Per serving (about 750 ml [3 cups] salad): 238 Cal, 6 g Total Fat, 1 g Sat Fat, 0 g Trans Fat, 221 mg Chol, 494 mg Sod, 21 g Carb, 8 g Sugar, 6 g Fib, 26 g Prot, 155 mg Calc.

for your information

This recipe calls for both grated orange zest and peeled orange—be sure to remove the necessary amount of zest from the orange before peeling it.

greek barley salad

serves 2

per serving

- ▲ **250 ml (1 cup) reduced-sodium vegetable broth**
- **2 ml (½ tsp) dried oregano**
- ▲ **125 ml (½ cup) quick-cooking barley**
- ▲ **½ green bell pepper, diced**
- ▲ **250 ml (1 cup) cherry tomatoes, halved**
- ▲ **1 Kirby (pickling) cucumber, chopped**
- ▲ **75 ml (⅓ cup) diced red onion**
- **30 ml (2 Tbsp) chopped fresh parsley**
- **15 ml (1 Tbsp) red-wine vinegar**
- **10 ml (2 tsp) olive oil**
- **1 ml (¼ tsp) black pepper**
- ▲ **60 ml (¼ cup) crumbled reduced fat feta cheese**

1 Bring broth and oregano to boil in small saucepan. Stir in barley. Reduce heat and cover. Simmer until barley is softened, 10–12 minutes. Remove from heat and let stand 5 minutes. Transfer to large bowl.

2 Add bell pepper, tomatoes, cucumber, onion, parsley, vinegar, oil, and black pepper to barley and toss to combine. Divide salad between 2 plates and sprinkle evenly with feta cheese.

Per serving (375 ml [1½ cup] salad and 30 ml [2 Tbsp] feta): 322 Cal, 9 g Total Fat, 2 g Sat Fat, 0 g Trans Fat, 6 mg Chol, 213 mg Sod, 51 g Carb, 6 g Sugar, 11 g Fib, 12 g Prot, 116 mg Calc

stay on track

Be sure to take advantage of the fact that almost all fruits have a ***PointsPlus*** value of ***0***. If you pack this salad up to take to the office, think ahead and tote along a banana or cup of sliced melon as well to help you stay satisfied throughout the day.

tortellini salad with tomatoes and broccoli

serves 2

8 PointsPlus® value per serving

- 130 g (4.5 oz) package fresh cheese tortellini
- ▲ 500 ml (2 cups) small broccoli florets
- 15 ml (1 Tbsp) balsamic vinegar
- 5 ml (1 tsp) olive oil
- 30 ml (2 Tbsp) grated Parmesan cheese
- ▲ 250 ml (1 cup) grape tomatoes, halved
- 6 pitted black olives (not cured in oil), sliced
- 30 ml (2 Tbsp) sliced fresh basil leaves
- 0.5 ml (1/8 tsp) black pepper

1 Cook tortellini according to package directions, adding broccoli during last 3 minutes of cooking. Drain and rinse under cold running water; set aside.

2 Meanwhile, combine vinegar, oil, and 15 ml (1 Tbsp) Parmesan in medium bowl. Add tortellini, broccoli, tomatoes, olives, and basil; toss to coat. Sprinkle salad with remaining 15 ml (1 Tbsp) cheese and pepper. Serve at once, or cover and refrigerate up to 24 hours and serve chilled.

Per serving (375 ml [1½ cups]): 290 Cal, 10 g Total Fat, 4 g Sat Fat, 0 g Trans Fat, 31 mg Chol, 404 mg Sod, 39 g Carb, 4 g Sugar, 5 g Fib, 14 g Prot, 210 mg Calc.

provençal stuffed tomatoes

provençal stuffed tomatoes

serves 4

per serving

- 125 ml (½ cup) water
- 1 ml (¼ tsp) salt
- ▲ 75 ml (⅓ cup) whole wheat couscous
- ▲ 4 very large beefsteak or heirloom tomatoes
- 15 ml (1 Tbsp) olive oil
- ▲ 1 small zucchini, finely diced
- ▲ ½ small onion, finely diced
- ▲ ½ small yellow bell pepper, finely diced
- ▲ 1 (398-ml [14 fl. oz]) can no-salt-added white beans, rinsed and drained
- ▲ 125 ml (½ cup) no-salt-added canned tomato sauce
- Pinch cayenne
- ▲ 75 ml (⅓ cup) crumbled reduced fat feta cheese
- 60 ml (¼ cup) sliced basil leaves

1 Bring water and salt to boil in small saucepan. Stir in couscous; cover and remove from heat. Let stand 5 minutes; fluff with fork.

2 Meanwhile, cut thin slice off top of each tomato and reserve. With spoon, scoop out seeds and pulp, leaving sturdy tomato shells. (Discard pulp and seeds or save for soup or sauce.)

3 Heat oil in large nonstick skillet over high heat. Add zucchini, onion, and bell pepper. Cook, stirring frequently, until vegetables soften, about 5 minutes. Add beans, tomato sauce, and cayenne; cook until heated through, about 2 minutes. Remove from heat and stir in couscous, feta, and basil. Spoon about 250 ml (1 cup) filling into each tomato shell and cover with reserved tops.

Per serving (1 stuffed tomato): 275 Cal, 6 g Total Fat, 1 g Sat Fat, 0 g Trans Fat, 5 mg Chol, 324 mg Sod, 44 g Carb, 8 g Sugar, 9 g Fib, 14 g Prot, 144 mg Calc.

for your information

Use 175 ml (¾ cup) leftover cooked brown rice or quinoa in place of the couscous, and this dish will come together in about 15 minutes with no change in the ***PointsPlus*** value.

apricot-glazed steak kebabs

serves 4

per serving

- ▲ **60 ml (¼ cup) reduced-sodium chicken broth**
- **30 ml (2 Tbsp) no-sugar-added apricot spread**
- **15 ml (1 Tbsp) reduced-sodium soy sauce**
- ▲ **450 g (1 lb) lean boneless sirloin steak, trimmed and cut into 2.5-cm (1-in) pieces**
- ▲ **4 large mushrooms, halved**
- ▲ **1 red onion, cut into 8 pieces**
- ▲ **1 small zucchini, cut into 8 pieces**

1 Spray broiler rack with nonstick spray; preheat broiler.

2 Mix broth, apricot spread, and soy sauce in small bowl until smooth.

3 Thread beef and vegetables on 4 (30-cm [12-in]) metal skewers, alternating beef and vegetables. Brush with half of broth mixture. Place skewers on the broiler rack and broil 12.5 cm (5 in) from heat for 4 minutes. Turn and brush with remaining broth mixture. Broil until meat and vegetables are browned and cooked through, 5–6 minutes.

Per serving (1 skewer): 201 Cal, 5 g Total Fat, 2 g Sat Fat, 0 g Trans Fat, 49 mg Chol, 197 mg Sod, 10 g Carb, 6 g Sugar, 1 g Fib, 28 g Prot, 30 mg Calc.

stay on track

Serve these savoury kebabs with quick-cooking brown rice; a 125-ml (½-cup) portion of cooked brown rice with each serving will increase the ***PointsPlus*** value by ***3***.

apricot-glazed steak kebabs

grilled bison sliders

serves 4

per serving

- 450 g (1 lb) ground lean bison (buffalo) meat
- ▲ 30 ml (2 Tbsp) finely chopped onion
- 5 ml (1 tsp) Worcestershire sauce
- 1 ml (1/4 tsp) salt
- 1 ml (1/4 tsp) black pepper
- 1 small (225-g [8-oz]) whole-grain baguette, cut into 16 slices

1 Spray grill rack with nonstick spray. Preheat grill to medium-high or prepare medium-high fire.

2 Place bison, onion, Worcestershire sauce, salt, and pepper in large bowl; mix gently just until combined. With damp hands, shape bison mixture into 8 (1.25-cm [1/2-in]) thick patties. Place patties on grill rack and grill until instant-read thermometer inserted into side of patties registers 70°C (160°F), about 4 minutes per side. Serve each slider between 2 slices of baguette.

Per serving (2 sliders): 280 Cal, 4 g Total Fat, 1 g Sat Fat, 0 g Trans Fat, 81 mg Chol, 528 mg Sod, 30 g Carb, 2 g Sugar, 3 g Fib, 30 g Prot, 7 mg Calc.

for your information

Bison meat is very lean and flavourful, and using it for mini slider burgers is a perfect way to enjoy it. It's readily available in supermarkets in some parts of the country, or you can look for it at grocery stores that specialize in natural foods or at butcher shops.

spicy pork and pineapple skewers

serves 4

per serving

- 30 ml (2 Tbsp) lime juice
- 30 ml (2 Tbsp) orange marmalade
- ▲ 450 g (1 lb) lean pork tenderloin, trimmed and cut into 20 chunks
- ▲ 16 (2.5-cm [1-in]) chunks fresh pineapple
- 6 ml (1¼ tsp) Jamaican jerk seasoning
- 1 ml (¼ tsp) salt

1 Spray broiler rack with nonstick spray; preheat broiler.

2 To make glaze, stir together lime juice and marmalade in small bowl until combined and set aside.

3 Combine pork, pineapple, jerk seasoning, and salt in medium bowl; toss to coat. Thread pork and pineapple alternately on 4 (30-cm [12-in]) metal skewers. Place skewers on broiler rack and broil 12.5 cm (5 in) from heat, turning every 2 minutes, until pork is browned, about 8 minutes. Brush kebabs with half of glaze and broil 1 minute more. Turn kebabs, brush with remaining glaze, and broil until glazed and pork is cooked through, about 1 minute longer.

Per serving (1 skewer): 162 Cal, 3 g Total Fat, 1 g Sat Fat, 0 g Trans Fat, 74 mg Chol, 584 mg Sod, 10 g Carb, 8 g Sugar, 0 g Fib, 24 g Prot, 11 mg Calc.

duck with red wine and rosemary

duck with red wine and rosemary

serves 4

per serving

4 (140-g [5-oz]) skinless boneless duck breasts

2 ml (½ tsp) salt

1 ml (¼ tsp) black pepper

5 ml (1 tsp) olive oil

2 shallots, finely chopped

10 ml (2 tsp) chopped fresh rosemary

75 ml (⅓ cup) red wine

30 ml (2 Tbsp) no-sugar-added cherry spread

▲ **4 fresh figs, halved**

1 Sprinkle duck with salt and pepper. Heat oil in large nonstick skillet over medium heat. Add duck to pan and cook until underside is golden, about 5 minutes. Turn duck. Sprinkle shallots around duck and cook just until duck is cooked through, about 5 minutes. Transfer duck to plate and keep warm, leaving shallots in skillet.

2 To make glaze, add rosemary to skillet and cook, stirring, until fragrant, about 30 seconds. Stir in wine, cherry spread, and any juices that have accumulated from cooked duck. Increase heat to medium-high and bring to simmer. Add figs and cook, stirring occasionally, until mixture is thick and syrupy, about 2 minutes.

3 Slice duck and serve with sauce and figs spooned on top.

Per serving (1 duck breast, 30 ml (2 Tbsp) glaze, and 1 fig): 279 Cal, 7 g Total Fat, 2 g Sat Fat, 0 g Trans Fat, 109 mg Chol, 375 mg Sod, 20 g Carb, 15 g Sugar, 2 g Fib, 29 g Prot, 36 mg Calc.

stay on track

Serve this delicious duck with a side of roasted butternut squash. Arrange 570-g (20-oz) peeled cut up butternut squash on a large baking sheet sprayed with nonstick spray. Lightly spray the squash with nonstick spray and bake in a preheated 230°C (450°F) oven until tender, 20 to 25 minutes.

grilled chicken with tropical salsa

serves 4

per serving

- ▲ **4 (140-g [5-oz]) skinless, boneless chicken breasts**
- **2 ml (½ tsp) ground cumin**
- **2 ml (½ tsp) salt**
- ▲ **1 L (4 cups) store-bought fresh fruit salad**
- ▲ **60 ml (¼ cup) chopped red onion**
- **45 ml (3 Tbsp) chopped fresh cilantro**
- ▲ **½ jalapeño pepper, seeded and minced**
- **15 ml (1 Tbsp) lime juice**

1 Sprinkle chicken with cumin and 1 ml (¼ tsp) salt. Spray ridged grill pan with nonstick spray and place over medium-high heat. Add chicken and cook until browned and cooked through, 5–6 minutes per side.

2 Meanwhile, to make salsa, finely dice fruit salad and place in large bowl. Add onion, cilantro, jalapeño, lime juice, and remaining 1 ml (¼ tsp) salt and toss. Serve salsa alongside chicken.

Per serving (1 piece chicken and 250 ml [1 cup] salsa): 250 Cal, 3 g Total Fat, 1 g Sat Fat, 0 g Trans Fat, 78 mg Chol, 375 mg Sod, 23 g Carb, 19 g Sugar, 3 g Fib, 30 g Prot, 19 mg Calc.

ultimate turkey burgers

serves 4

per serving

- ▲ **500 g (1 lb) ground skinless turkey breast**
- ▲ **1 large celery stalk, chopped**
- ▲ **2 scallions, chopped**
- **45 ml (3 Tbsp) quick-cooking oats**
- **30 ml (2 Tbsp) mild cayenne pepper sauce + more for serving**
- ▲ **4 light whole wheat hamburger rolls**
- **30 ml (2 Tbsp) reduced-fat blue cheese dressing**

1 Mix turkey, celery, scallions, oats, and 30 ml (2 Tbsp) pepper sauce in medium bowl just until combined. With damp hands, gently form mixture into 4 1.25-cm (½-in) thick patties.

2 Spray ridged grill pan with nonstick spray and place over medium heat. Add patties and cook until instant-read thermometer inserted into side of each patty registers 75°C (165°F), about 5 minutes per side.

3 Place burgers in buns and drizzle each with 7 ml (½ Tbsp) dressing. Serve with pepper sauce on the side.

Per serving (1 burger with 7 ml [1½ tsp] dressing): 275 Cal, 5 g Total Fat, 0 g Sat Fat, 0 g Trans Fat, 45 mg Chol, 353 mg Sod, 29 g Carb, 5 g Sugar, 5 g Fib, 33 g Prot, 64 mg Calc.

stay on track

Try starting your meal with a filling salad of thinly sliced raw kale, sliced red onion, and halved cherry tomatoes tossed with lemon juice and salt and pepper.

peppered tuna steak with artichokes

serves 4

per serving

- 5 ml (1 tsp) mixed peppercorns, crushed
- 2 ml (½ tsp) fennel seed, crushed
- 1 ml (¼ tsp) salt
- ▲ 450 g (1 lb) tuna steak 1.25-cm (½-in) thick
- ▲ 680 g (24 oz) artichoke hearts
- ▲ 1 (250-g [8-oz]) bag mixed baby greens
- ▲ 200 g (7 oz) jarred roasted red bell peppers (not packed in oil), drained and sliced
- ▲ 250 ml (1 cup) canned no-salt-added chickpeas, rinsed and drained
- 90 ml (6 Tbsp) fat-free Italian dressing
- 4 lemon wedges

1 Mix peppercorns, fennel seed, and salt in small bowl. Sprinkle mixture over both sides of tuna steak. Spray ridged grill pan with nonstick spray and set over medium heat. Add tuna and cook until browned but still pink in centre, 2–3 minutes per side.

2 Meanwhile, quarter artichoke hearts if they are large. Combine artichokes, greens, bell peppers, and chickpeas in large bowl. Drizzle with dressing and toss to coat. Divide among 4 plates.

3 Transfer tuna to cutting board and cut into 12 slices. Top each portion with 3 slices of tuna and serve at once with lemon wedges.

Per serving (575 ml [2⅓ cups] salad and 3 slices tuna): 350 Cal, 9 g Total Fat, 1 g Sat Fat, 0 g Trans Fat, 42 mg Chol, 775 mg Sod, 35 g Carb, 5 g Sugar, 15 g Fib, 34 g Prot, 148 mg Calc.

peppered tuna steak with artichokes

salmon cakes with dijon-herb sauce

serves 4

per serving

- **22 ml (1½ Tbsp) apple cider vinegar**
- **15 ml (1 Tbsp) olive oil**
- **15 ml (1 Tbsp) Dijon mustard**
- **10 ml (2 tsp) chopped fresh chives**
- **5 ml (1 tsp) chopped fresh tarragon or 1 ml (¼ tsp) dried**
- ▲ **2 (213 g [7.5 oz]) cans wild salmon, drained, skin removed and discarded**
- **60 ml (¼ cup) fat-free mayonnaise**
- ▲ **3 scallions, chopped**
- **45 ml (3 Tbsp) + 60 ml (¼ cup) whole wheat panko (Japanese bread crumbs)**
- ▲ **1 large egg white, lightly beaten**
- ▲ **1 L (4 cups) frisée lettuce or mixed lettuces**

1 To make sauce, whisk together vinegar, oil, mustard, chives, and tarragon in small bowl. Cover and refrigerate until ready to serve.

2 Preheat broiler. Spray small baking sheet with nonstick spray.

3 Place salmon in large bowl. Mash salmon and bones with fork until fairly smooth. Add mayonnaise, scallions, 45 ml (3 Tbsp) panko, and egg white and stir to combine. With damp hands, shape mixture into 4 patties. Put remaining 60 ml (¼ cup) panko on sheet of wax paper. Coat patties with crumbs and place on prepared baking sheet. Broil 10 cm (4 in) from heat until crisp and golden, about 4 minutes per side.

4 Divide greens among 4 plates. Top each portion with 1 salmon cake and drizzle with 15 ml (1 Tbsp) sauce.

Per serving (1 salmon cake, 250 ml [1 cup] greens, and 15 ml [1 Tbsp] sauce): 252 Cal, 9 g Total Fat, 1 g Sat Fat, 0 g Trans Fat, 87 mg Chol, 682 mg Sod, 16 g Carb, 4 g Sugar, 3 g Fib, 28 g Prot, 302 mg Calc.

shrimp and asparagus frittata

serves 4

per serving

- 10 ml (2 tsp) canola oil
- ▲ 4 scallions, sliced
- ▲ 115 g (¼ lb) mushrooms, chopped
- ▲ 225 g (½ lb) thin asparagus, trimmed and cut into 2.5-cm (1-in) pieces
- 0.5 ml (⅛ tsp) salt
- 1 ml (¼ tsp) black pepper
- ▲ 225 g (½ lb) small peeled and deveined cooked shrimp
- ▲ 500 ml (2 cups) fat-free egg substitute
- ▲ 375 ml (1½ cups) shredded part skim mozzarella cheese
- 30 ml (2 Tbsp) chopped fresh basil

1 Heat oil in large nonstick skillet over medium-high heat. Add scallions, mushrooms, asparagus, salt, and pepper. Cook, stirring frequently, until vegetables are tender, about 7 minutes. Stir in shrimp.

2 Reduce heat to medium and pour egg substitute over vegetables and shrimp. Cook until set, lifting edges frequently with spatula to let uncooked egg flow underneath, about 3 minutes.

3 Sprinkle mozzarella over frittata. Cover skillet. Reduce heat to low and cook until cheese melts, about 3 minutes. Sprinkle with basil and cut into 4 wedges.

Per serving (1 wedge): 269 Cal, 10 g Total Fat, 4 g Sat Fat, 0 g Trans Fat, 137 mg Chol, 724 mg Sod, 9 g Carb, 5 g Sugar, 2 g Fib, 36 g Prot, 462 mg Calc.

stay on track

You might think of eggs as just a breakfast staple, but they're terrific for quick and satisfying dinners, too. Try serving this protein-packed, veggie-loaded main course with quick-cooking barley sprinkled with a little soy sauce; a 125-ml (½-cup) portion of cooked barley has a ***PointsPlus*** value of **3**.

easy scampi with edamame

serves 4

per serving

- ▲ 375 ml (1½ cup) frozen shelled edamame
- ▲ 450 g (1 lb) large peeled and deveined shrimp
- 2 ml (½ tsp) salt
- 10 ml (2 tsp) olive oil
- 10 ml (2 tsp) unsalted butter
- 5 garlic cloves, sliced
- 0.5 ml (⅛ tsp) red pepper flakes
- 60 ml (¼ cup) white wine
- 30 ml (2 Tbsp) chopped fresh parsley

1 Bring small saucepan of water to boil. Add edamame and cook until tender, about 5 minutes. Drain and set aside.

2 Meanwhile, sprinkle shrimp with 1 ml (¼ tsp) of salt. Heat oil in a large skillet over high heat. Add shrimp and cook until lightly browned and just opaque in centre, 2–3 minutes per side. Transfer to plate.

3 Add butter to skillet and melt over medium-high heat. Add garlic and cook, stirring, until very fragrant and tender, about 2 minutes. Stir in pepper flakes, edamame, shrimp, and remaining 1 ml (¼ tsp) salt. Pour in wine and cook, stirring, until most of liquid has evaporated, about 1 minute. Sprinkle with parsley and serve.

Per serving (250 ml [1 cup]): 217 Cal, 8 g Total Fat, 2 g Sat Fat, 0 g Trans Fat, 226 mg Chol, 549 mg Sod, 5 g Carb, 1 g Sugar, 2 g Fib, 29 g Prot, 81 mg Calc.

stay on track

Linguine is the classic accompaniment to garlicky shrimp scampi; a 125-ml (½-cup) serving of cooked whole wheat linguine will increase the ***PointsPlus*** value by ***2***.

curried rice noodles with seafood

serves 4

per serving

- 250 g (1/2 lb) rice noodles
- 10 ml (2 tsp) canola oil
- ▲ 1 (450-g [1-lb]) bag frozen seafood medley (shrimp, calamari, scallops, shelled mussels, and imitation crabmeat), thawed
- ▲ 250 ml (1 cup) thawed frozen peas
- ▲ 4 scallions, thinly sliced
- 10 ml (2 tsp) curry powder
- ▲ 125 ml (1/2 cup) reduced-sodium chicken broth
- 0.5 ml (1/8 tsp) black pepper

1 Cook rice noodles according to package directions; drain.

2 Meanwhile, heat oil in large skillet over high heat. Add seafood medley and cook, stirring, just until heated through, about 3 minutes. Add peas and scallions; cook until scallions are tender, about 1 minute. Add curry powder and cook, stirring constantly, until fragrant, about 30 seconds.

3 Add noodles, broth, and pepper and cook until heated through, about 2 minutes.

Per serving (425 ml [1 3/4 cup]): 424 Cal, 3 g Total Fat, 0 g Sat Fat, 0 g Trans Fat, 260 mg Chol, 667 mg Sod, 63 g Carb, 2 g Sugar, 5 g Fib, 35 g Prot, 41 mg Calc.

mussels marinara

mussels marinara

serves 4

per serving

- 170 g (6 oz) linguine
- 10 ml (2 tsp) olive oil
- ▲ 1 onion, chopped
- 6 garlic cloves, sliced
- ▲ 1 (796-ml [28-fl. oz]) can peeled plum tomatoes, drained and chopped
- 125 ml (1/2 cup) red wine
- 0.5 ml (1/8 tsp) red pepper flakes
- ▲ 910 g (2 lb) mussels, scrubbed and debearded
- 60 ml (1/4 cup) chopped fresh basil or parsley

1 Cook pasta according to package directions, omitting salt.

2 Meanwhile, heat oil in Dutch oven over medium-high heat. Add onion and garlic. Cook, stirring occasionally, until golden, about 7 minutes. Add tomatoes, wine, and pepper flakes; bring to boil. Reduce heat and simmer 2 minutes.

3 Add mussels. Cover and simmer until mussels just open, about 5 minutes. Discard any mussels that do not open. Stir in basil.

4 Drain pasta and toss immediately with about 125 ml (1/2 cup) sauce from Dutch oven. Divide pasta among 4 large, deep bowls. Top pasta evenly with remaining sauce and mussels.

Per serving (500 ml [2 cups] mussels in shells and 175 ml [3/4 cup] pasta with sauce): 345 Cal, 5 g Total Fat, 1 g Sat Fat, 0 g Trans Fat, 28 mg Chol, 719 mg Sod, 49 g Carb, 9 g Sugar, 4 g Fib, 20 g Prot, 92 mg Calc.

udon and scallops in miso-ginger broth

serves 4

per serving

- 10 ml (2 tsp) Asian (dark) sesame oil
- 2 garlic cloves, minced
- 15 ml (1 Tbsp) minced peeled fresh ginger
- ▲ 750 ml (3 cups) low-sodium vegetable broth
- 500 ml (2 cups) water
- 30 ml (2 Tbsp) light miso
- ▲ 170 g (6 oz) whole-grain udon noodles
- ▲ 500 g (1 lb) sea scallops
- ▲ 1 (142-g [4.75-oz]) bag baby spinach
- ▲ 3 scallions, sliced

1 Heat oil in Dutch oven over medium heat. Add garlic and ginger. Cook, stirring, until fragrant, about 1 minute. Add broth, water, and miso; bring to boil. Add udon noodles and return to boil. Cook over medium heat, stirring occasionally, 3 minutes.

2 Add scallops and spinach. Return to boil and simmer until scallops are just opaque in centre and noodles are tender, about 4 minutes. Remove from heat and sprinkle with scallions.

Per serving (about 5 scallops with 250 ml [1 cup] broth and noodles): 321 Cal, 4 g Total Fat, 0 g Sat Fat, 0 g Trans Fat, 37 mg Chol, 779 mg Sod, 42 g Carb, 4 g Sugar, 5 g Fib, 27 g Prot, 82 mg Calc.

for your information

Whole-grain udon, available at supermarkets and natural foods stores, is a delicious pasta for this soup. You can also substitute 100% buckwheat soba noodles or thin whole-grain spaghetti.

udon and scallops in miso-ginger broth

tofu and vegetables in coconut sauce

serves 4

per serving

- 250 ml (1 cup) light (reduced-fat) coconut milk
- 15 ml (1 Tbsp) Asian fish sauce
- 5 ml (1 tsp) brown sugar
- 10 ml (2 tsp) cornstarch
- 2 ml (½ tsp) Thai red curry paste
- 10 ml (2 tsp) peanut or canola oil
- ▲ 595 g (21 oz) low-fat firm tofu, drained and cut into 1.25-cm (½-in) cubes
- ▲ 500 ml (2 cups) small broccoli florets
- ▲ 1 small zucchini, halved lengthwise and thinly sliced
- ▲ 1 red bell pepper, cut into strips
- 30 ml (2 Tbsp) chopped fresh cilantro

1 Stir together coconut milk, fish sauce, brown sugar, cornstarch, and curry paste in small bowl until smooth; set aside.

2 Heat oil in large skillet over high heat. Add tofu and cook, stirring frequently, until golden, about 4 minutes. Transfer to bowl.

3 Add broccoli, zucchini, and bell pepper to skillet. Cook, stirring constantly, until vegetables are crisp-tender, about 3 minutes. Add tofu and coconut milk mixture. Cook, stirring constantly, until sauce thickens, about 1 minute. Sprinkle with cilantro.

Per serving (310 ml [1¼ cup]): 175 Cal, 9 g Total Fat, 1 g Sat Fat, 0 g Trans Fat, 0 mg Chol, 436 mg Sod, 12 g Carb, 3 g Sugar, 3 g Fib, 15 g Prot, 301 mg Calc.

spaghetti with feta and walnuts

serves 4

per serving

- ▲ 125 g (½ lb) whole wheat spaghetti
- ▲ 750 ml (3 cups) small cauliflower florets
- 5 ml (1 tsp) olive oil
- 2 shallots, thinly sliced
- ▲ 250 ml (1 cup) reduced-sodium chicken broth
- Pinch red pepper flakes
- ▲ 250 ml (1 cup) (115 g [4 oz]) crumbled low fat feta cheese
- ▲ 4 scallions, thinly sliced (white and light green parts only)
- 60 ml (¼ cup) chopped toasted walnuts

1 Cook spaghetti according to package directions, omitting salt; add cauliflower during minutes of cooking.

2 Meanwhile, heat oil in large nonstick skillet over medium heat. Add shallots and cook, stirring occasionally, until tender, about 2 minutes. Stir in broth and pepper flakes and bring to boil.

3 Drain spaghetti and cauliflower. Add to skillet; then add feta and scallions. Reduce heat to low and toss mixture until spaghetti is coated. Serve sprinkled with walnuts.

Per serving (about 375 ml [1½ cup] spaghetti mixture and 15 ml [1 Tbsp] walnuts): 348 Cal, 10 g Total Fat, 3 g Sat Fat, 0 g Trans Fat, 8 mg Chol, 560 mg Sod, 51 g Carb, 5 g Sugar, 8 g Fib, 18 g Prot, 149 mg Calc.

stay on track

Finish your meal with a refreshing salad of peeled and chopped oranges sprinkled with sliced mint leaves.

pear and roquefort pizza

pear and roquefort pizza

serves 4

per serving

- 1 (285-g [10-oz]) prebaked thin pizza crust
- 30 ml (2 Tbsp) balsamic vinegar
- 15 ml (1 Tbsp) olive oil
- 1 small garlic clove, minced
- 10 ml (2 tsp) honey mustard
- 1 ml (¼ tsp) salt
- 1 ml (¼ tsp) black pepper
- ▲ 1 bag (142 g [4.75 oz]) mesclun salad greens
- ▲ 1 ripe pear, cored and cut into 12 slices
- 75 ml (⅓ cup) crumbled Roquefort or other blue cheese

1 Preheat oven to 230°C (450°F). Place pizza crust on baking sheet. Bake until lightly browned and crisp, about 7 minutes.

2 Meanwhile, whisk together vinegar, oil, garlic, honey mustard, salt, and pepper in large bowl. Add salad greens and toss to coat. Spoon salad over warm crust. Top with pear and sprinkle with Roquefort. Cut pizza into 4 wedges and serve at once.

Per serving (1 wedge): 327 Cal, 11 g Total Fat, 3 g Sat Fat, 0 g Trans Fat, 10 mg Chol, 784 mg Sod, 46 g Carb, 8 g Sugar, 4 g Fib, 11 g Prot, 179 mg Calc.

YOUR THIRD MONTH

—

Ready in 30 Minutes or Less

breakfasts

Western-Style Coddled Eggs
Eggs with Red Flannel Hash
Tomato and Ricotta Frittata for Two
Mushroom-Bacon Omelette
Oat Flapjacks with Blueberry Sauce
Apple Pie Waffles
Florentine Breakfast Crêpes
Maple-Nut Granola

lunches

Falafel Sandwiches with Spicy Tahini
Vegetable Summer Rolls
Potato Lovers' Soup with Crispy Bacon
Manhattan Clam Chowder with Vegetables
Pasta e Fagioli Soup
Creamy Cauliflower Soup with Paprika and Chives
Tex-Mex Eight-Layer Beef Salad
Waldorf-Style Pasta Salad
Classic Bistro Salad with Poached Eggs
Bulgur Salad with Pear and Blue Cheese
Beef and Lettuce Rolls with Mango Salsa
Pepper Jack Quesadillas with Shrimp and Spinach

dinners

Flank Steak with Garlicky Potato Rosti
Filet Mignon with Red Wine and Herb Sauce
Summer Steak Kebabs
Savoury Beef and Lentil Burgers
Beef, Black Bean, and Beer Chili
Pork Marsala with Gorgonzola
Honey-Glazed Pork Tenderloin with Sweet Potatoes
Penne with Ham, Peas, and Goat Cheese
Herb-Crusted Lamb Chops with Snap Peas
Shish Kebabs with Pomegranate
Pesto-Stuffed Chicken Breasts
Thai Red Curry with Chicken and Vegetables
Linguine Puttanesca with Chicken and Artichokes
Chicken with Israeli Couscous Salad
Moroccan Couscous with Chicken and Dates
Creole Oven-Fried Chicken
Grilled Drumsticks with Molasses Barbecue Sauce
Braised Chicken Thighs with Feta and Olives
Wild Mushroom and Sausage Risotto
Hearty Kale and Sausage Soup
Hoisin Duck Wraps with Spicy Slaw
Wild Salmon en Papillote
Catfish Escabèche with Cilantro Brown Rice
Garlicky Spaghetti with Shrimp and White Beans
Broiled Lobster Tails with Mango Salsa
Ancho Chili Verde with Tempeh
Cold Noodles with Tofu and Spicy Peanut Sauce
Sicilian-Style Penne with Eggplant
Polenta and Kale Gratin

western-style coddled eggs

serves 4

per serving

- **5 ml (1 tsp) canola oil**
- ▲ **175 ml (3/4 cup) diced lean cooked ham**
- ▲ **1 small green bell pepper, chopped**
- ▲ **2 scallions, chopped**
- ▲ **4 large eggs**
- ▲ **175 ml (3/4 cup) shredded lwo fat Cheddar cheese**
- **0.5 ml (1/8 tsp) black pepper**

1 Preheat oven to 160°C (325°F). Spray 4 (180-ml [6-fl. oz]) ovenproof ramekins or custard cups with nonstick spray.

2 Heat oil in medium nonstick skillet over medium-high heat. Add ham and cook, stirring occasionally, until browned, about 3 minutes. Add bell pepper and scallions. Cook, stirring occasionally, until vegetables are tender, about 5 minutes. Divide bell pepper mixture among ramekins. Carefully break 1 egg into each ramekin.

3 Place ramekins on small baking sheet and bake just until eggs begin to set, about 15 minutes. Evenly sprinkle Cheddar and black pepper on each egg. Bake until egg whites are opaque and yolks are set, 4–5 minutes.

Per serving **(1 ramekin): 169 Cal, 9 g Total Fat, 3 g Sat Fat. 0 g Trans Fat, 204 mg Chol, 468 mg Sod, 3 g Carb, 1 g Sugar, 1 g Fib, 18 g Prot, 144 mg Calc.**

stay on track

Want to add some whole grains to your breakfast? Accompany each serving of this protein-packed dish with a slice of reduced-calorie rye bread for an additional ***PointsPlus*** value of **2** per serving.

western-style coddled eggs

eggs with red flannel hash

serves 2

per serving

- 7 ml (1½ tsp) olive oil
- ▲ 1 small (115-g [4-oz]) red potato, chopped
- ▲ 1 small cooked red beet or 125 ml (½ cup) drained canned beets, chopped
- ▲ ½ small onion, chopped
- 1 garlic clove, finely chopped
- 1 ml (¼ tsp) salt
- ▲ 2 large eggs

1 Heat 3 ml (¾ tsp) oil in medium nonstick skillet over medium heat. Add potato; cover and cook, stirring once, just until beginning to soften, about 5 minutes. Add beet, onion, garlic, and salt. Cover and cook, stirring occasionally, until vegetables are tender and lightly browned, about 5 minutes.

2 Heat remaining 3 ml (¾ tsp) oil in second medium nonstick skillet over medium heat. Break eggs into skillet. Cover and cook until whites are firm, 3–4 minutes. Divide hash between 2 plates; top each serving with 1 egg.

Per serving **(125 ml [½ cup] hash and 1 egg): 158 Cal, 8 g Total Fat, 2 g Sat Fat, 0 g Trans Fat, 215 mg Chol, 376 mg Sod, 14 g Carb, 3 g Sugar, 2 g Fib, 8 g Prot, 37 mg Calc.**

stay on track

Start or finish your breakfast with a refreshing wedge of cantaloupe or honeydew melon sprinkled with lime juice and you'll feel satisfied longer.

tomato and ricotta frittata for two

serves 2

7 PointsPlus® value per serving

- 10 ml (2 tsp) olive oil
- ▲ 1 small (115-g [4-oz]) red potato, scrubbed and diced
- ▲ 3 scallions, sliced
- ▲ 2 large eggs
- ▲ 2 large egg whites
- 0.5 ml (1/8 tsp) salt
- ▲ 1 tomato, chopped
- ▲ 75 ml (1/3 cup) light ricotta cheese
- ▲ 60 ml (1/4 cup) shredded part skim mozzarella cheese

1 Heat oil in medium nonstick skillet over medium-high heat. Add potato and 2 scallions. Cook, stirring frequently, until vegetables are tender, about 6 minutes.

2 Meanwhile, beat eggs, egg whites, and salt in medium bowl until frothy. Pour eggs over vegetables and reduce heat to medium. Cook, lifting edges frequently with spatula to let uncooked egg flow underneath, until eggs are almost set, 2–3 minutes.

3 Dot top with ricotta and sprinkle with mozzarella. Sprinkle tomato and remaining scallion over top. Cover and reduce heat to low. Cook until mozzarella melts, about 2 minutes. Cut frittata in half and slide each half onto a plate.

Per serving **(1/2 of frittata): 261 Cal, 13 g Total Fat, 4 g Sat Fat, 0 g Trans Fat, 204 mg Chol, 452 mg Sod, 16 g Carb, 5 g Sugar, 2 g Fib, 18 g Prot, 233 mg Calc.**

for your information

For firmer eggs, you can place the skillet under a preheated broiler for a minute or two before topping the frittata with cheese.

mushroom-bacon omelette

serves 1

per serving

- 5 ml (1 tsp) canola oil
- 2 slices lower sodium turkey bacon
- ▲ 250 ml (1 cup) sliced mixed mushrooms
- 1 garlic clove, sliced
- ▲ 125 ml (½ cup) fat-free egg substitute
- Pinch black pepper
- ▲ 30 ml (2 Tbsp) shredded fat-free Swiss cheese

1 Heat 2 ml (½ tsp) oil in medium skillet over medium heat. Add bacon and cook until crisped, about 3 minutes per side. Transfer to paper towels to drain. Add mushrooms and garlic to skillet. Cook, stirring frequently, until mushrooms are browned, about 6 minutes. Transfer to small bowl. Chop bacon and add to bowl.

2 Wipe out skillet. Add remaining 2 ml (½ tsp) oil and heat over medium-high heat. Pour in egg substitute and swirl to cover bottom of pan. Sprinkle with pepper and cook, stirring gently, until underside is set, about 30 seconds. Continue to cook 30 seconds more, lifting edges frequently with spatula to let uncooked egg flow underneath.

3 Spread mushroom mixture and Swiss cheese evenly over half of omelette; fold other half over filling. Slide omelette onto plate.

Per serving (1 omelette): 211 Cal, 10 g Total Fat, 2 g Sat Fat, 0 g Trans Fat, 28 mg Chol, 744 mg Sod, 5 g Carb, 3 g Sugar, 0 g Fib, 24 g Prot, 465 mg Calc.

oat flapjacks with blueberry sauce

serves 2

per serving

- ▲ 125 ml (½ cup) fresh or thawed frozen unsweetened blueberries
- 7 ml (1½ tsp) confectioners' sugar
- 15 ml (1 Tbsp) water
- 125 ml (½ cup) old-fashioned rolled oats
- 7 ml (1½ tsp) packed brown sugar
- 2 ml (½ tsp) baking powder
- 0.5 ml (⅛ tsp) baking soda
- Pinch salt
- ▲ 60 ml (¼ cup) plain fat-free yogourt
- ▲ 37 ml (2½ Tbsp) skim milk
- ▲ 30 ml (2 Tbsp) fat-free egg substitute
- 2 ml (½ tsp) canola oil

1 To make sauce, combine blueberries, confectioners' sugar, and water in small saucepan. Cook, stirring occasionally, over medium-low heat until slightly thickened, about 5 minutes. Keep warm.

2 To make flapjacks, place oats, brown sugar, baking powder, baking soda, and salt in food processor; pulse until oats are finely ground. Transfer to large bowl and add yogourt, milk, and egg substitute; stir just until blended.

3 Heat oil on nonstick griddle or in large nonstick skillet over medium heat. Pour batter by 60-ml (¼-cup) measures onto griddle, making 4 flapjacks. Cook until bubbles on top burst and undersides are golden brown, 3–4 minutes. Flip and cook 3–4 minutes longer. Serve flapjacks with blueberry sauce.

Per serving (2 flapjacks and 45 ml [3 Tbsp] sauce): 185 Cal, 3 g Total Fat, 0 g Sat Fat, 0 g Trans Fat, 1 mg Chol, 347 mg Sod, 35 g Carb, 19 g Sugar, 3 g Fib, 6 g Prot, 126 mg Calc.

apple pie waffles

apple pie waffles

serves 4

per serving

- ▲ **5 firm apples, such as Gala or Fuji, peeled and cored**
- **5 ml (1 tsp) unsalted butter**
- **45 ml (3 Tbsp) sugar**
- **2 ml (½ tsp) apple pie spice or cinnamon**
- **125 ml (½ cup) whole wheat flour**
- **125 ml (½ cup) all-purpose flour**
- **5 ml (1 tsp) baking powder**
- **1 ml (¼ tsp) baking soda**
- **0.5 ml (⅛ tsp) salt**
- ▲ **125 ml (½ cup) skim milk**
- ▲ **1 large egg**
- **10 ml (2 tsp) canola oil**

1 Slice 4 apples. Melt butter in large nonstick skillet over medium-high heat. Add sliced apples to skillet with 15 ml (1 Tbsp) sugar and 1 ml (¼ tsp) apple pie spice. Cover and cook until apples are tender, about 5 minutes. Uncover and cook until most of liquid evaporates, about 3 minutes. Set aside.

2 Spray waffle iron with nonstick spray and heat according to manufacturer's directions. Combine whole wheat flour, all-purpose flour, baking powder, baking soda, salt, remaining 30 ml (2 Tbsp) sugar, and remaining 1 ml (¼ tsp) apple pie spice in large bowl. Whisk milk, egg, and oil together in small bowl. Stir milk mixture into flour mixture just until combined. Shred remaining apple on box grater and fold into batter.

3 Pour 125 ml (½ cup) batter onto heated waffle iron, close, and cook according to manufacturer's directions. Repeat with remaining batter to make total of 4 waffles. Serve topped with cooked apple.

Per serving **(1 waffle and 125 ml [½ cup] cooked apple): 297 Cal, 5 g Total Fat, 1 g Sat Fat, 0 g Trans Fat, 57 mg Chol, 318 mg Sod, 59 g Carb, 29 g Sugar, 5 g Fib, 7 g Prot, 84 mg Calc.**

florentine breakfast crêpes

serves 2

per serving

- ▲ **1 (300-g [10.5-oz]) package frozen chopped spinach**
- **60 ml (¼ cup) water**
- **5 ml (1 tsp) olive oil**
- ▲ **225 g (½ lb) cremini mushrooms, sliced**
- **115 g (4 oz) fat-free cream cheese**
- **0.5 ml (⅛ tsp) ground nutmeg**
- **4 (17.5-cm [7-in]) ready-to-use crêpes, warmed according to package directions**

1 Combine spinach and water in large nonstick skillet; bring to boil. Reduce heat to medium-low, cover, and cook until spinach is thawed and heated through, about 8 minutes. Drain in sieve and press with back of spoon to remove excess liquid.

2 Wipe out skillet. Heat oil over medium-high heat. Add mushrooms and cook, stirring occasionally, until lightly browned and have released their liquid, 5–6 minutes.

3 Add spinach and cook, stirring occasionally, until heated through, 2–3 minutes. Add cream cheese and nutmeg. Cook, stirring frequently, until cheese melts, 1–2 minutes. Spoon 150 ml (⅔ cup) filling onto each crêpe and roll up. Serve at once.

Per serving **(2 filled crêpes): 203 Cal, 4 g Total Fat, 0 g Sat Fat, 0 g Trans Fat, 16 mg Chol, 790 mg Sod, 24 g Carb, 10 g Sugar, 2 g Fib, 16 g Prot, 306 mg Calc.**

maple-nut granola

serves 10

per serving

- 375 ml (1½ cups) old-fashioned rolled oats
- ▲ 125 ml (½ cup) unprocessed wheat bran
- 60 ml (¼ cup) sesame seeds
- 125 ml (½ cup) cashews or walnuts, coarsely chopped
- 75 ml (5 Tbsp) maple syrup
- 2 ml (½ tsp) vanilla extract
- 1 ml (¼ tsp) cinnamon
- 175 ml (¾ cup) thinly sliced dried apricots
- 175 ml (¾ cup) raisins

1 Place rack in middle of oven; preheat oven to 180°C (350°F).

2 Spread oats, bran, and sesame seeds on rimmed baking sheet. Bake, stirring with metal spatula every 3 minutes, until golden brown, 9–10 minutes.

3 Meanwhile, combine nuts, maple syrup, vanilla, and cinnamon in medium bowl. Add oat mixture and toss to combine. Spread mixture evenly onto baking sheet. Bake, stirring every 3 minutes, until dark golden brown, 9–10 minutes. Transfer mixture to large bowl; stir in apricots and raisins. Let cool.

Per serving **(125 ml [½ cup]): 200 Cal, 6 g Total Fat, 1 g Sat Fat, 0 g Trans Fat, 0 mg Chol, 13 mg Sod, 35 g Carb, 21 g Sugar, 4 g Fib, 4 g Prot, 35 mg Calc.**

stay on track

Having a quick, healthy go-to cereal on hand for rushed mornings is invaluable. You can serve each 125-ml (½-cup) portion of this granola with 125 ml (½ cup) skim milk, increasing the per-serving ***PointsPlus*** value by ***1***. Store granola in an airtight container on the counter up to 2 weeks or in the refrigerator up to 3 months.

falafel sandwiches with spicy tahini

serves 2

per serving

- **60 ml (¼ cup) falafel mix**
- **60 ml (4 Tbsp) water**
- **1 whole wheat pita (15 cm [6 in]), halved**
- ▲ **125 ml (½ cup) sliced romaine lettuce**
- ▲ **125 ml (½ cup) diced tomato**
- **11 ml (2¼ tsp) tahini paste**
- **7 ml (1½ tsp) lemon juice**
- **½ small garlic clove, minced**
- **1 ml (¼ tsp) hot pepper sauce, or to taste**
- **Pinch salt**

1 Spray broiler pan with nonstick spray; preheat broiler.

2 Combine falafel mix and 45 ml (3 Tbsp) water in medium bowl. Let stand until water is absorbed, 2–3 minutes. Form mixture into 4 balls and place on broiler pan 2.5 cm (1 in) apart. Flatten balls into 2.5-cm (1-in) patties and spray with nonstick spray. Broil 12.5 cm (5 in) from heat until golden brown, about 2 minutes per side.

3 Fill each pita half with 60 ml (¼ cup) lettuce, 60 ml (¼ cup) tomato, and 2 falafel patties.

4 Stir together tahini, lemon juice, garlic, pepper sauce, and salt in small cup. Whisk in remaining 15 ml (1 Tbsp) water. Drizzle sauce into pita halves and serve at once.

Per serving **(1 filled pita half and 15 ml [1 Tbsp] tahini sauce): 193 Cal, 6 g Total Fat, 1 g Sat Fat, 0 g Trans Fat, 0 mg Chol, 485 mg Sod, 32 g Carb, 2 g Sugar, 4 g Fib, 7 g Prot, 34 mg Calc.**

for your information

You'll find falafel mix in the international foods section of most supermarkets.

vegetable summer rolls

serves 2

- 30 ml (2 Tbsp) reduced-sodium soy sauce
- 15 ml (1 Tbsp) rice vinegar
- 5 ml (1 tsp) sugar
- 15 ml (1 Tbsp) water
- 30 g (1 oz) thin rice noodles
- 5 ml (1 tsp) Asian (dark) sesame oil
- 8 rice paper wrappers (15 cm [6 in])
- ▲ 1 carrot, shredded
- ▲ 2 scallions, thinly sliced
- 60 ml (1/4 cup) unsalted peanuts, chopped
- 60 ml (1/4 cup) cilantro leaves
- 8 basil leaves

1 Whisk together soy sauce, vinegar, sugar, and water in small bowl; set aside.

2 Place rice noodles in medium bowl and add enough boiling water to cover. Let stand until noodles soften, about 10 minutes. Drain; rinse under cold running water and drain again. Cut noodles into 5-cm (2-in) lengths and toss with oil.

3 To assemble rolls, dip rice paper wrappers, one at a time, in bowl of warm water until softened, about 45 seconds; transfer to clean kitchen towel. Place one-eighth of noodles, carrot, scallions, peanuts, cilantro, and basil in centre of each wrapper. Fold in two opposite sides; then roll up to enclose filling. Repeat until all wrappers are filled. Serve with soy sauce mixture for dipping.

Per serving (4 rolls and 30 ml [2 Tbsp] dipping sauce): 343 Cal, 12 g Total Fat, 2 g Sat Fat, 0 g Trans Fat, 0 mg Chol, 600 mg Sod, 51 g Carb, 6 g Sugar, 3 g Fib, 11 g Prot, 43 mg Calc.

potato lovers' soup with crispy bacon

’ soup with

per serving

aked

l

▲ 675 ml (ed-sodium chicken broth

1 ml (¼ tsp) salt

1 ml (¼ tsp) hot pepper sauce

▲ 175 ml (¾ cup) light cream (5% M.F.)

1 Leaving skin on, coarsely chop potatoes; set aside.

2 Cook bacon in large nonstick saucepan over medium heat until crisp. Drain on paper towels and set aside. Pour off and discard all but 5 ml (1 tsp) of drippings.

3 Add garlic and half of scallions to drippings in saucepan. Cook over medium heat, stirring occasionally, until softened, about 3 minutes. Add broth, salt, pepper sauce, and potatoes, mashing potatoes with wooden spoon to break them up slightly. Bring mixture to boil. Reduce heat and simmer until heated through, 2–3 minutes.

4 Stir in cream and return to simmer. Serve soup sprinkled with crumbled bacon and remaining scallions.

Per serving **(375 ml [1½ cup]): 262 Cal, 5 g Total Fat, 2 g Sat Fat, 0 g Trans Fat, 21 mg Chol, 395 mg Sod, 42 g Carb, 5 g Sugar, 4 g Fib, 10 g Prot, 119 mg Calc.**

for your information

This hearty soup is especially convenient if you have leftover baked potatoes on hand. If you don’t, preheat the oven to 220°C (425°F), pierce each potato a few times with a fork, and place on the middle rack of the oven. Bake until tender, 45 to 50 minutes.

manhattan clam chowder with vegetables

serves 4

per serving

- 5 ml (1 tsp) canola oil
- ▲ 1 red onion, chopped
- 1 (30-g [1-oz]) slice Canadian bacon, finely diced
- ▲ 2 celery stalks, thinly sliced
- ▲ 1 (435-g [14½-oz]) can no-salt-added diced tomatoes
- 250 ml (1 cup) bottled clam juice
- ▲ 2 medium (170-g [6-oz]) red potatoes, scrubbed and diced
- ▲ 2 (142 g [5 oz]) cans whole baby clams in juice
- ▲ 255 g (9 oz) frozen vegetable medley
- 5 ml (1 tsp) chopped fresh thyme or 1 ml (¼ tsp) dried

1 Heat oil in medium nonstick saucepan over medium heat. Add onion, bacon, and celery and cook, stirring occasionally, until vegetables are tender, about 6 minutes.

2 Add tomatoes, clam juice, and potatoes; bring to boil. Reduce heat and cover. Simmer until potatoes are tender, about 15 minutes.

3 Add clams and vegetable medley; return to boil. Reduce heat and simmer, covered, until vegetables are tender, about 5 minutes. Stir in thyme.

Per serving (310 ml [1¼ cup]): 245 Cal, 4 g Total Fat, 1 g Sat Fat, 0 g Trans Fat, 63 mg Chol, 671 mg Sod, 35 g Carb, 10 g Sugar, 6 g Fib, 18 g Prot, 170 mg Calc.

for your information

Canadian bacon, made from pork loin, is very lean and flavourful and is an excellent alternative to conventional bacon. If you have some leftover after making this chowder, you can try it with eggs. Each 30-g (1-oz) slice has a ***PointsPlus*** value of ***1***.

pasta e fagioli soup

serves 4

- 10 ml (2 tsp) olive oil
- ▲ 1 (450-g [1-lb]) bag coleslaw mix
- ▲ 1 small onion, chopped
- 2 garlic cloves, sliced
- ▲ 750 ml (3 cups) reduced-sodium chicken broth
- ▲ 1 (398-ml [14½-fl. oz]) can no-salt-added cannellini (white kidney) beans, rinsed and drained
- ▲ 175 ml (¾ cup) whole wheat ditali pasta, elbow macaroni, or small shells
- 1 ml (¼ tsp) salt
- 0.5 ml (⅛ tsp) red pepper flakes
- 500 ml (2 cups) water
- 10 ml (2 tsp) chopped fresh thyme leaves

1 Heat oil in a large Dutch oven over medium heat. Add coleslaw mix, onion, and garlic; cook, stirring constantly, until coleslaw is wilted, about 3 minutes. Reduce heat and cover. Cook, stirring occasionally, until onion is tender, about 6 minutes.

2 Add broth, beans, pasta, salt, pepper flakes, and water; bring to boil. Reduce heat and simmer, covered, until macaroni is tender, about 12 minutes. Stir in thyme.

Per serving (500 ml [2 cups]): 237 Cal, 5 g Total Fat, 1 g Sat Fat, 0 g Trans Fat, 0 mg Chol, 260 mg Sod, 39 g Carb, 2 g Sugar, 9 g Fib, 13 g Prot, 114 mg Calc.

▲ Florets fr[illegible]
(about 1.3 L [5 cu

▲ 750 ml ([illegible]) [illegible]duced [illegible]
chicken broth

▲ 1 small onion, chopped

▲ 1 celery stalk, chopped

250 ml (1 cup) water

▲ 250 ml (1 cup) light cream
(5% M.F)

2 ml (½ tsp) smoked or
sweet paprika

45 ml (3 Tbsp) chopped fresh
chives

3 Pour s[illegible]
Return soup to pan and st[illegible]
stirring occasionally, over medium heat until hot,
about 3 minutes. Sprinkle with paprika and chives.

Per serving (about 375 ml [1½ cup]): 114 Cal, 4 g Total Fat, 2 g Sat Fat, 0 g Trans Fat, 20 mg Chol, 159 mg Sod, 13 g Carb, 7 g Sugar, 4 g Fib, 7 g Prot, 134 mg Calc.

stay on track

This light soup is perfect to serve alongside an easy salad of chopped lettuce and chickpeas drizzled with lemon juice; a 125-ml (½-cup) serving of chickpeas per person has a ***PointsPlus*** value of ***3***.

tex-mex eight-layer beef salad

serves 4

- ▲ 340 g (3/4 lb) ground lean beef (7% fat or less)
- ▲ 1/2 onion, diced
- 15 ml (1 Tbsp) chili powder
- 1 ml (1/4 tsp) salt
- ▲ 1 L (4 cups) shredded romaine lettuce
- ▲ 3 plum tomatoes, diced
- ▲ 250 ml (1 cup) canned no-salt-added pinto beans, rinsed and drained
- ▲ 1 small jicama, peeled and cut into strips
- ▲ 4 scallions, thinly sliced
- ▲ 250 ml (1 cup) fat-free salsa
- ▲ 75 ml (1/3 cup) fat-free sour cream
- 30 ml (2 Tbsp) chopped fresh cilantro

1 Set large nonstick skillet over medium heat. Add beef and onion. Cook, breaking beef apart with wooden spoon, until beef is no longer pink, about 4 minutes. Stir in chili powder and salt. Remove from heat and set aside.

2 Layer lettuce, tomatoes, beans, jicama, and scallions in large glass salad bowl or large round casserole dish. Top with warm beef mixture, salsa, and sour cream. Sprinkle with cilantro and serve at once.

Per serving (375 ml [1½ cup]): 265 Cal, 5 g Total Fat, 2 g Sat Fat, 0 g Trans Fat, 53 mg Chol, 495 mg Sod, 31 g Carb, 7 g Sugar, 10 g Fib, 23 g Prot, 114 mg Calc.

for your information

Jicama (HEE-kuh-muh) is a round root vegetable with a thin light brown skin and ivory-coloured flesh. Its sweetness and crunch make it a great addition to salads, but you can substitute cucumber or yellow bell pepper for the jicama in this recipe, if you like.

waldorf-style pasta salad

serves 2

- ▲ 125 ml (½ cup) small whole wheat pasta shells
- 15 ml (1 Tbsp) fat-free mayonnaise
- ▲ 15 ml (1 Tbsp) plain fat-free Greek yogourt
- ½ small shallot, finely chopped
- 7 ml (1½ tsp) lemon juice
- 0.5 ml (⅛ tsp) salt
- ▲ 125 ml (½ cup) chopped skinless boneless roast turkey breast
- ▲ 1 Gala or other firm sweet apple, cored and cut into 1.25-cm (½-in) chunks
- ▲ 125 ml (½ cup) seedless red grapes, halved
- ▲ 1 celery stalk, finely chopped
- 30 ml (2 Tbsp) golden raisins
- 15 ml (1 Tbsp) toasted chopped walnuts

1 Cook pasta according to package directions, omitting salt. Drain; rinse under cold running water until cool and drain again.

2 Whisk mayonnaise, yogourt, shallot, lemon juice, and salt in large bowl until blended. Add turkey, apple, grapes, celery, raisins, and pasta; toss to coat. Sprinkle with walnuts.

Per serving (about 375 ml [1½ cups] salad and 7 ml [1½ tsp] walnuts): 273 Cal, 3 g Total Fat, 1 g Sat Fat, 0 g Trans Fat, 40 mg Chol, 233 mg Sod, 50 g Carb, 25 g Sugar, 5 g Fib, 14 g Prot, 40 mg Calc.

poached eggs

serves 2

per serving

5 ml (1 tsp) canola oil

2 (30-g [1-oz]) slices Canadian bacon, diced

▲ 500 ml (2 cups) roughly chopped frisée lettuce

▲ 500 ml (2 cups) chopped romaine lettuce

▲ 125 ml (½ cup) grape tomatoes, quartered

10 ml (2 tsp) + 15 ml (1 Tbsp) white-wine vinegar

▲ 2 large eggs

5 ml (1 tsp) olive oil

1 shallot, finely chopped

▲ 30 ml (2 Tbsp) reduced-sodium chicken broth

5 ml (1 tsp) Dijon mustard

2 ml (½ tsp) dried tarragon

0.5 ml (⅛ tsp) salt

1 Fill a medium skillet halfway full with water and bring to boil over high heat.

2 Meanwhile, heat canola oil in medium nonstick skillet over medium heat. Add bacon and cook, stirring, until browned, about 4 minutes. Transfer bacon to large bowl. Add frisée, romaine, and tomatoes.

3 Reduce heat until water in skillet just simmers and add 10 ml (2 tsp) vinegar. Crack eggs into simmering water and reduce heat to medium-low. Poach eggs until whites are set but yolks are still soft, about 2 minutes. With slotted spoon, gently transfer eggs to plate lined with paper towels.

4 Wipe out nonstick skillet. Heat olive oil in skillet over medium heat. Add shallot and cook, stirring, until softened, about 2 minutes. Add broth and simmer until liquid is almost completely evaporated, about 1 minute. Remove from heat and stir in mustard, tarragon, salt, and remaining 15 ml (1 Tbsp) vinegar. Pour over salad and toss to coat. Divide between 2 plates. Top each salad with 1 poached egg.

Per serving (500 ml [2 cups] salad and 1 egg): 201 Cal, 12 g Total Fat, 3 g Sat Fat, 0 g Trans Fat, 231 mg Chol, 734 mg Sod, 9 g Carb, 2 g Sugar, 3 g Fib, 15 g Prot, 79 mg Calc.

bulgur salad with pear and blue cheese

blue cheese

serves 2

per serving

- 250 ml (1 cup) water
- ▲ 150 ml (2/3 cup) bulgur
- 5 ml (1 tsp) safflower or canola oil
- ▲ 1 large ripe pear, cored and diced
- 125 ml (1/2 cup) reduced-fat crumbled blue cheese
- ▲ 2 stalks celery, diced
- ▲ 1 small head Belgian endive, cut crosswise in half
- ▲ 60 ml (1/4 cup) sliced red onion
- 15 ml (1 Tbsp) apple cider vinegar
- 30 ml (2 Tbsp) chopped fresh parsley
- 0.5 ml (1/8 tsp) black pepper

1 Bring water to boil in small saucepan. Stir in bulgur; remove pan from heat. Cover and let stand until water is absorbed, about 25 minutes.

2 Fluff bulgur with fork; add oil and fluff again. Transfer bulgur to large bowl and add remaining ingredients. Toss to combine and serve warm or at room temperature.

Per serving (560 ml [2 1/4 cups]) 345 Cal, 9 g Total Fat, 4 g Sat Fat, 0 g Trans Fat, 20 mg Chol, 334 mg Sod, 58 g Carb, 14 g Sugar, 14 g Fib, 15 g Prot, 259 mg Calc.

stay on track

Eating lunch at your desk or on the road? Pack up a serving of this filling salad along with a banana, and you should feel satisfied until dinner.

beef and lettuce rolls with mango salsa

serves 2

per serving

- ▲ **½ mango, peeled, pitted, and diced**
- ▲ **125 ml (½ cup) diced red bell pepper**
- ▲ **2 scallions, chopped**
- **30 ml (2 Tbsp) chopped fresh cilantro**
- ▲ **5 ml (1 tsp) seeded diced jalapeño pepper**
- **10 ml (2 tsp) lime juice**
- **0.5 ml (⅛ tsp) salt**
- **15 ml (1 Tbsp) no-sugar-added apricot fruit spread**
- **15 ml (1 Tbsp) hoisin sauce**
- **1 garlic clove, minced**
- ▲ **250 g (½ lb) lean beef tenderloin, trimmed and cut on the diagonal into 8 slices**
- ▲ **4 large green-leaf lettuce leaves**

1 To make salsa, combine mango, bell pepper, scallions, cilantro, jalapeño, lime juice, and salt in small bowl; set aside.

2 Line broiler rack with foil; preheat broiler.

3 Combine fruit spread, hoisin sauce, and garlic in medium bowl. Add beef; toss to coat. Thread beef on 2 (20-cm [8-in]) metal skewers. Place skewers on broiler rack. Broil 12.5 cm (5 in) from heat until beef is browned, about 3 minutes per side. Remove beef from skewers.

4 Place lettuce leaves on work surface. Divide beef and salsa evenly among leaves. Fold two long sides of each leaf over filling. Starting from short end, roll up each leaf to enclose filling.

Per serving (2 rolls): 265 Cal, 7 g Total Fat, 3 g Sat Fat, 0 g Trans Fat, 67 mg Chol, 344 mg Sod, 24 g Carb, 16 g Sugar, 3 g Fib, 26 g Prot, 58 mg Calc.

pepper jack quesadillas with shrimp and spinach

serves 2

7 PointsPlus® value per serving

- 5 ml (1 tsp) canola oil
- ▲ ½ onion, thinly sliced
- ▲ 500 ml (2 cups) baby spinach leaves
- ▲ 115 g (¼ lb) peeled cooked small or medium shrimp, chopped
- 4 (17.5-cm [7-in]) reduced-sodium whole wheat flour tortillas
- ▲ 125 ml (½ cup) shredded fat-free pepper Jack cheese

1 Preheat oven to 260°C (500°F). Spray baking sheet with nonstick spray.

2 Heat oil in medium nonstick skillet over medium heat. Add onion and cook, stirring occasionally, until golden, about 5 minutes. Add spinach and cook, stirring, until wilted, about 1 minute. Remove from heat and stir in shrimp.

3 Place 2 tortillas on work surface. Top each with 30 ml (2 Tbsp) pepper Jack, half of shrimp mixture, and 30 ml (2 Tbsp) more cheese. Cover with remaining tortillas and press down gently.

4 Place quesadillas on prepared baking sheet. Spray tops lightly with nonstick spray and bake until lightly browned, about 4 minutes per side. Cut into wedges and serve.

Per serving (1 quesadilla): 239 Cal, 10 g Total Fat, 0 g Sat Fat, 0 g Trans Fat, 3 mg Chol, 831 mg Sod, 34 g Carb, 3 g Sugar, 21 g Fib, 22 g Prot, 427 mg Calc.

stay on track

Serve these delicious quesadillas topped with your favourite fat-free salsa and chopped fresh cilantro.

simply zero

No matter what situation you find yourself in when you need just a bite of something, there's a ***0*** ***PointsPlus*** value snack to satisfy.

Note: ***PointsPlus*** values for these snack ideas were arrived at by entering all ingredients into Weight Watchers' online Recipe Builder. Although each of these ideas has a ***PointsPlus*** value of ***0***, eating several of them in one day could accumulate ***PointsPlus*** values. Let your weight loss be your guide.

Want something to pack for the office?

• Get your taste buds going with 6 pieces of giardiniera (pickled Italian vegetables).

• Munch on 4 baby carrots dipped into 7 ml (½ Tbsp) plain fat-free yogourt.

• Stir together a quick and crunchy slaw using 125 ml (½ cup) packaged coleslaw mix, 7 ml (1 Tbsp) plain fat-free yogourt, and salt and black pepper to taste.

• Make a salad of thinly sliced raw zucchini tossed with lemon zest and juice, fresh chopped dill, and salt and black pepper to taste.

Need to find an on-the-go snack at a corner deli or gas station?

• Choose one of the fruits that you'll find near the cash register at most convenience stores: an apple, banana, or orange.

• Look for individual-serving fruit cups packed in water or cups of unsweetened applesauce.

• Refresh yourself with a club soda, seltzer water, diet soda, or unsweetened iced or hot tea.

Looking to fight an afternoon slump?

• Freeze brewed coffee in an ice cube tray. Purée the coffee cubes in a blender with 45 ml (3 Tbsp) skim milk and 15-30 ml (1-2 Tbsp) of water (if needed) to make a "pick-me-up" slushy.

• Dip cucumber slices into 15 ml (1 Tbsp)

fat-free mayonnaise stirred together with a pinch of lemon zest and a few drops lemon juice.

• Fill a halved baby bell pepper with 45 ml (3 Tbsp) fat-free cottage cheese; sprinkle with a few drops of hot pepper sauce, if you like.

• Snack on 45 ml (3 Tbsp) fat-free salsa spooned into 6 Belgian endive leaves.

Need to take the edge off your hunger before dinner?

• Keep a small bowl of cherries, strawberries, or blueberries nearby to nibble on while you're making dinner.

• Dip a couple of celery sticks or a few radishes or cucumber slices into 15 ml (1 Tbsp) of Dijon mustard.

• Munch on a crunchy, kosher dill pickle.

Gotta snack while you watch TV?

• Nibble 125 ml (½ cup) plain air-popped popcorn sprinkled with sea salt. Add chili powder or curry powder if you like.

• Munch on sweet and flavourful sugar snap peas—you can eat them raw!

• Enjoy an orange, clementine, or tangerine; peeling and segmenting the fruit will keep your hands busy.

• Try pomegranate seeds, a tart and delicious antioxidant-rich snack.

Want to relax with a hot drink?

• Make ginger tea: Pour 250 ml (1 cup) of boiling water over 2 thin slices of fresh ginger and let steep 5 minutes.

• Add a sprig of fresh mint to your favourite herbal tea to make it even more flavourful.

• Enjoy a cup of unsweetened coffee with up to 45 ml (3 Tbsp) skim milk.

• Sip hot beef broth with a few added drops each of soy sauce and lemon juice.

Need a healthy snack to pack for a road trip?

• Segment a tangerine and pack it in a zip-close plastic bag. Since it's already peeled, you can enjoy this snack even if you're the driver.

• Grape tomatoes are easily portable and super sweet.

• If licorice candy is your usual road trip snack, replace it with strips of fresh fennel. You'll get a refreshing anise flavour along with lots of natural crunch.

• Pick up a few packs of presliced apples, available in the produce section of most supermarkets.

flank steak with garlicky potato rosti

serves 4

per serving

- ▲ **1 lean flank steak (450 g [1 lb]), trimmed**
- **10 ml (2 tsp) Cajun seasoning**
- ▲ **1 large sweet onion, cut into 4 wedges**
- **15 ml (3 tsp) canola oil**
- **3 garlic cloves, finely chopped**
- ▲ **2 russet potatoes (225-g [8-oz]), scrubbed and shredded**
- **1 ml (¼ tsp) salt**

1 Spray broiler rack with nonstick spray; preheat broiler.

2 Sprinkle steak with Cajun seasoning; place steak on broiler rack. Arrange onion wedges around steak; drizzle onion with 5 ml (1 tsp) oil. Broil 12.5 cm (5 in) from heat until instant-read thermometer inserted into centre of steak registers 63°C (145°F) for medium, 5–6 minutes per side.

3 Meanwhile, heat remaining 10 ml (2 tsp) oil in large nonstick skillet over medium heat. Add garlic and cook, stirring, until fragrant, about 30 seconds. Stir in potatoes and salt; press down into flat cake. Cover and cook until golden on bottom, about 5 minutes. With rubber spatula, cut rosti into fourths. Turn each piece and cook, covered, until golden on bottom, about 5 minutes longer.

4 Transfer steak to cutting board. Let stand 5 minutes; cut into 16 slices. Serve with onion and potato rosti.

Per serving (4 slices steak, 1 piece onion, and 1 piece potato rosti): 297 Cal, 10 g Total Fat, 3 g Sat Fat, 0 g Trans Fat, 42 mg Chol, 471 mg Sod, 25 g Carb, 2 g Sugar, 2 g Fib, 27 g Prot, 43 mg Calc.

flank steak with garlicky potato rosti

filet mignon with red wine and herb sauce

serves 4

6 PointsPlus® value per serving

- ▲ **4 (115-g [¼-lb]) lean filet mignon steaks, trimmed**
- **1 ml (¼ tsp) salt**
- **1 ml (¼ tsp) black pepper**
- **5 ml (1 tsp) olive oil**
- **1 large shallot, minced**
- **175 ml (¾ cup) dry red wine**
- **30 ml (2 Tbsp) reduced-fat garlic-and-herb spreadable cheese**
- **15 ml (1 Tbsp) chopped fresh parsley**

1 Sprinkle steaks with salt and pepper. Heat large cast-iron skillet over medium-high heat. Add steaks and cook until instant-read thermometer inserted into centre of each steak registers 63°C (145°F) for medium, about 3 minutes per side. Transfer to cutting board and cover loosely with foil.

2 To make sauce, heat oil in skillet over medium heat. Add shallot and cook, stirring occasionally, until softened, about 2 minutes. Stir in wine. Increase heat to medium-high and bring to boil. Cook, scraping up browned bits from bottom of skillet, until mixture is reduced to 75 ml (⅓ cup), about 4 minutes. Remove skillet from heat. Add cheese, stirring until melted. Stir in parsley.

3 Pour sauce over steaks and serve at once.

Per serving (1 steak with 22 ml [1½ Tbsp] sauce): 232 Cal, 9 g Total Fat, 3 g Sat Fat, 0 g Trans Fat, 72 mg Chol, 239 mg Sod, 3 g Carb, 1 g Sugar, 0 g Fib, 25 g Prot, 49 mg Calc.

summer steak kebabs

serves 4

per serving

- ▲ **450 g (1 lb) lean beef sirloin, trimmed and cut into 3-cm (1¼-in) cubes**
- ▲ **3 ears corn on the cob, each cut crosswise into 3 pieces**
- ▲ **2 peaches, pitted and cut into 3-cm (1¼-in) chunks**
- ▲ **2 red bell peppers, cut into large squares**
- **15 ml (1 Tbsp) olive oil**
- **7 ml (1½ tsp) chopped fresh rosemary or 2 ml (½ tsp) dried**
- **2 ml (½ tsp) salt**

1 Set ridged grill pan over medium-high heat or preheat grill to medium-high or prepare medium-high fire.

2 Thread beef, corn, peaches, and bell peppers alternately on 4 (30-cm [12-in]) metal skewers and brush with oil. Sprinkle with rosemary and salt. Grill, turning frequently, until beef is cooked to desired doneness and peaches and vegetables are browned, about 12 minutes on grill pan or 8 minutes on grill.

Per serving (1 skewer): 283 Cal, 9 g Total Fat, 3 g Sat Fat, 0 g Trans Fat, 49 mg Chol, 358 mg Sod, 22 g Carb, 5 g Sugar, 4 g Fib, 29 g Prot, 24 mg Calc.

for your information

There's no reason to wait for summer to try these delicious kebabs: Instead of fresh corn, you can use thawed frozen corn on the cob from the freezer section of your supermarket. To thread pieces of corn, pierce each piece through the centre of the cob and twist the skewer gently.

savoury beef and lentil burgers

serves 4

per serving

- ▲ 340 g (¾ lb) ground lean beef (7% fat or less)
- ▲ 1 (540-ml [18-fl. oz]) can lentils, rinsed and drained (yields about 375 ml [1 ½ cups] lentils)
- ▲ 75 ml (⅓ cup) plain fat-free Greek yogourt
- ▲ 30 ml (2 Tbsp) finely chopped onion
- 15 ml (1 Tbsp) finely chopped fresh parsley
- 30 ml (2 Tbsp) whole wheat bread crumbs
- 7 ml (1½ tsp) curry powder
- 1 ml (¼ tsp) salt
- 5 ml (1 tsp) canola oil
- ▲ 4 (43-g [1½-oz]) light whole-grain hamburger buns
- ▲ 250 ml (1 cup) thinly sliced lettuce leaves
- ▲ 1 plum tomato, chopped

1 Mix beef, lentils, yogourt, onion, parsley, bread crumbs, curry powder, and salt in large bowl just until combined. With damp hands, form mixture into 4 (2.5-cm [1-in]-thick) burgers.

2 Heat oil in large nonstick skillet over medium heat. Add burgers and cook until instant-read thermometer inserted into side of each burger registers 75°C (165°F), about 6 minutes per side.

3 Serve burgers on buns topped with lettuce and tomato.

Per serving (1 burger): 351 Cal, 8 g Total Fat, 3 g Sat Fat, 0 g Trans Fat, 51 mg Chol, 573 mg Sod, 41 g Carb, 7 g Sugar, 12 g Fib, 30 g Prot, 83 mg Calc.

beef, black bean, and beer chili

serves 4

per serving

- 5 ml (1 tsp) canola oil
- ▲ 340 g (¾ lb) ground lean beef (7% fat or less)
- ▲ 1 small onion, diced
- 3 garlic cloves, minced
- 15 ml (1 Tbsp) chili powder
- ▲ 1 (398-ml [14-fl. oz]) can no-salt-added black beans, rinsed and drained
- ▲ 1 (414-ml [14½-fl. oz]) can diced tomatoes with jalapeño peppers
- 250 ml (1 cup) light beer
- 2 ml (½ tsp) salt

1 Heat oil in large saucepan over medium-high heat. Add beef and cook, breaking beef apart with wooden spoon, until no longer pink, about 4 minutes. Add onion, garlic, and chili powder; cook, stirring constantly, until fragrant, about 1 minute.

2 Add beans, diced tomatoes, beer, and salt. Bring to boil; reduce heat and simmer until chili is slightly thickened, 12–15 minutes.

Per serving (250 ml [1 cup]): 258 Cal, 6 g Total Fat, 2 g Sat Fat, 0 g Trans Fat, 51 mg Chol, 422 mg Sod, 23 g Carb, 3 g Sugar, 7 g Fib, 24 g Prot, 87 mg Calc.

stay on track

If you like, prepare a plate of ***0 PointsPlus*** value garnishes that diners can use to top their chili: Sliced scallions, chopped fresh cilantro, chopped tomato, chopped red onion, shredded lettuce, and lime wedges are some classics.

pork marsala with gorgonzola

pork marsala with gorgonzola

serves 4

per serving

- ▲ **1 (450-g [1-lb]) pork tenderloin, trimmed and cut on diagonal into 8 slices**
- **1 ml (¼ tsp) salt**
- **1 ml (¼ tsp) black pepper**
- **10 ml (2 tsp) olive oil**
- ▲ **225 g (½ lb) cremini mushrooms, sliced**
- **2 shallots, sliced**
- **3 garlic cloves, sliced**
- **75 ml (⅓ cup) Marsala wine**
- ▲ **250 ml (1 cup) reduced-sodium chicken broth**
- **60 ml (¼ cup) (55 g [2 oz]) crumbled Gorgonzola cheese**

1 Place pork slices between 2 pieces of wax paper and pound with wooden mallet or rolling pin to 1.25-cm (½-in) thickness. Sprinkle pork with salt and pepper.

2 Heat oil in large skillet over medium-high heat. Add 4 slices pork to skillet and cook until browned and cooked through, 2–3 minutes per side. Transfer to plate and keep warm. Repeat with remaining pork.

3 Add mushrooms, shallots, and garlic to skillet. Cook, stirring frequently, until mushrooms soften, about 5 minutes. Add wine; cook until liquid evaporates and mushrooms begin to brown, 5–6 minutes longer. Add broth and cook 3 minutes. Add Gorgonzola and reserved pork and any accumulated juices on plate. Cook, stirring, until cheese melts, about 1 minute.

Per serving (2 pieces pork and 75 ml (⅓ cup) mushroom mixture): 265 Cal, 10 g Total Fat, 4 g Sat Fat, 0 g Trans Fat, 75 mg Chol, 476 mg Sod, 9 g Carb, 3 g Sugar, 0 g Fib, 29 g Prot, 123 mg Calc.

for your information

Enjoy this dish the classic way by serving it alongside wide egg noodles sprinkled with parsley (125 ml [½ cup] cooked egg noodles for each serving will increase the ***PointsPlus*** value by ***3***).

honey-glazed pork tenderloin with sweet potatoes

serves 4

5 PointsPlus® value per serving

- 125 ml (½ cup) orange juice
- ▲ 60 ml (¼ cup) reduced-sodium chicken broth
- 15 ml (1 Tbsp) honey
- 10 ml (2 tsp) Dijon mustard
- 7 ml (1½ tsp) chopped fresh sage or 2 ml (½ tsp) dried
- ▲ 1 (450-g [1-lb]) lean pork tenderloin, trimmed
- 2 ml (½ tsp) salt
- 1 ml (¼ tsp) black pepper
- ▲ 450 g (1 lb) sweet potatoes, peeled and cut into 2.5-cm (1-in) pieces

1 Whisk orange juice, chicken broth, honey, mustard, and sage together in small bowl.

2 Sprinkle pork with salt and pepper. Spray Dutch oven with nonstick spray and set over medium-high heat. Add pork and cook, turning occasionally, until browned, about 4 minutes. Add sweet potatoes and orange juice mixture; bring to boil. Reduce heat and cover. Simmer until pork is cooked through and sweet potatoes are fork-tender, about 15 minutes.

3 Transfer pork to cutting board and cut into 12 slices. Serve with sweet potatoes and sauce.

Per serving (3 slices pork, 125 ml (½ cup) potatoes, and 15 ml [1 Tbsp] sauce): 227 Cal, 3 g Total Fat, 1 g Sat Fat, 0 g Trans Fat, 62 mg Chol, 449 mg Sod, 25 g Carb, 8 g Sugar, 3 g Fib, 24 g Prot, 36 mg Calc.

stay on track

If you're a pork fan, you'll want to get to know pork tenderloin better. It's one of the leanest cuts available and one of the lowest in ***PointsPlus*** values.

penne with ham, peas, and goat cheese

serves 4

per serving

- ▲ **225 g (½ lb) whole wheat penne**
- ▲ **250 ml (1 cup) shelled fresh or frozen peas**
- **2 ml (½ tsp) olive oil**
- **4 (30-g [1-oz]) slices Canadian bacon, chopped**
- ▲ **½ small onion, diced**
- ▲ **1 (225-g [8-oz]) bag fresh trimmed sugar-snap peas**
- **85 g (3 oz) fresh herbed goat cheese, crumbled**
- **0.5 ml(⅛ tsp) red pepper flakes**

1 Cook penne according to package directions, omitting salt and adding peas during last 3 minutes of cooking. Drain, reserving 250 ml (1 cup) of cooking liquid.

2 Meanwhile, heat oil in large skillet over medium-high heat. Add bacon and onion. Cook, stirring occasionally,.until onion is lightly browned, 4–5 minutes. Add sugar-snap peas and cook, stirring frequently, until sugar-snaps are bright green, about 3 minutes.

3 Add pasta, peas, goat cheese, and 125 ml (½ cup) of reserved cooking liquid to skillet. Reduce heat to medium-low and cook, stirring, until cheese melts, about 1 minute. If mixture is dry, add more cooking liquid, a few tablespoons at a time, until pasta is creamy. Remove skillet from heat, stir in pepper flakes, and serve at once.

Per serving (about 310 ml [1¼ cups]): 391 Cal, 9 g Total Fat, 4 g Sat Fat, 0 g Trans Fat, 26 mg Chol, 556 mg Sod, 56 g Carb, 7 g Sugar, 9 g Fib, 22 g Prot, 93 mg Calc.

herb-crusted lamb chops with snap peas

serves 4

per serving

4 garlic cloves, minced
7 ml (1½ tsp) dried herbes de Provence
15 ml (3 tsp) olive oil
2 ml (½ tsp) salt
▲ 4 (115-g [¼-lb]) lean boneless loin lamb chops, trimmed
▲ 500 ml (2 cups) sugar-snap peas
7 ml (1½ tsp) grated lemon zest
7 ml (1½ tsp) lemon juice
15 ml (1 Tbsp) chopped fresh dill

1 Combine garlic, herbes de Provence, 10 ml (2 tsp) oil, and 1 ml (¼ tsp) salt in small bowl. Rub mixture over lamb chops and let stand 5 minutes.

2 Heat remaining 5 ml (1 tsp) oil in large skillet over medium heat. Add lamb chops and cook until instant-read thermometer inserted into side of each chop, but not touching bone, registers 63°C (145°F) for medium, 3–4 minutes per side. Transfer lamb chops to plate and keep warm.

3 Put sugar-snap peas in steamer basket set over 2.5 cm (1 in) of boiling water. Cover tightly and steam until bright green and tender, about 4 minutes. Immediately transfer to bowl and toss with lemon zest and juice, dill, and remaining 1 ml (¼ tsp) salt. Serve with lamb chops.

Per serving (1 lamb chop and 125 ml [½ cup] snap peas): 194 Cal, 10 g Total Fat, 3 g Sat Fat, 0 g Trans Fat, 64 mg Chol, 349 mg Sod, 4 g Carb, 1 g Sugar, 1 g Fib, 21 g Prot, 33 mg Calc.

herb-crusted lamb chops with snap peas

shish kebabs with pomegranate

serves 4

per serving

- ▲ **60 ml (¼ cup) reduced-sodium chicken broth**
- **30 ml (2 Tbsp) pomegranate molasses**
- **2 ml (½ tsp) salt**
- ▲ **450 g (1 lb) lean boneless leg of lamb, trimmed and cut into 2.5-cm (1-in) pieces**
- ▲ **1 red onion, cut into 8 pieces**
- ▲ **1 green bell pepper, cut into 8 pieces**
- ▲ **125 ml (½ cup) pomegranate seeds for garnish (optional)**

1 Spray broiler rack with nonstick spray; preheat broiler.

2 Combine broth, pomegranate molasses, and salt in small bowl.

3 Thread lamb, onion, and bell pepper on 4 (30-cm [12-in]) metal skewers, alternating lamb and vegetables. Brush with half of broth mixture. Place skewers on broiler rack and broil 12.5 cm (5 in) from heat 4 minutes. Turn and brush with remaining broth mixture. Broil until lamb and vegetables are browned and cooked though, 5–6 minutes. Garnish with pomegranate seeds, if using.

Per serving (1 skewer): 226 Cal, 6 g Total Fat, 3 g Sat Fat, 0 g Trans Fat, 85 mg Chol, 340 mg Sod, 17 g Carb, 11 g Sugar, 2 g Fib, 25 g Prot, 39 mg Calc.

for your information

Sweet-tart pomegranate molasses is a popular Middle Eastern ingredient and widely available in specialty grocery stores. Thawed frozen cranberry juice concentrate is a good alternative.

pesto-stuffed chicken breasts

serves 4

per serving

- **60 ml (1/4 cup) crumbled goat cheese**
- **15 ml (1 Tbsp) pesto**
- **4 pitted black olives (not cured in oil), chopped**
- **15 ml (1 Tbsp) chopped fresh parsley**
- ▲ **4 (140-g [5-oz]) skinless boneless chicken breasts**
- **5 ml (1 tsp) olive oil**

1 To make filling, combine goat cheese, pesto, olives, and parsley in small bowl.

2 Make a pocket in side of each chicken breast by inserting sharp paring knife into thickest part and cutting to form a small pocket (do not cut all the way through breast). Using fingers, gently enlarge pocket. Stuff 22 ml (1½ Tbsp) filling into each breast. Close pockets with toothpicks.

3 Heat oil in large nonstick skillet over medium heat. Add chicken and cook until browned and cooked through, 6–7 minutes per side. Remove and discard toothpicks.

Per serving (1 stuffed chicken breast): 205 Cal, 8 g Total Fat, 3 g Sat Fat, 0 g Trans Fat, 83 mg Chol, 167 mg Sod, 1 g Carb, 0 g Sugar, 0 g Fib, 30 g Prot, 38 mg Calc.

thai red curry with chicken and vegetables

serves 4

per serving

- ▲ **450 g (1 lb) skinless boneless chicken breast, cut into 2.5-cm (1-in) chunks**
- **1 ml (¼ tsp) salt**
- **10 ml (2 tsp) canola oil**
- ▲ **1 yellow bell pepper, thinly sliced**
- ▲ **6 scallions, cut into 2.5-cm (1-in) pieces**
- **12 ml (2½ tsp) Thai red curry paste**
- **5 ml (1 tsp) sugar**
- **1 (400-ml [14-fl oz]) can light (reduced-fat) coconut milk**
- ▲ **375 g (12 oz) fresh cauliflower florets (about 800 ml [3 ⅕ cups])**
- ▲ **170 g (6 oz) bag shredded carrots (about 325 ml [1 ⅓ cups])**
- **125 ml (½ cup) torn fresh basil or cilantro leaves**

1 Sprinkle chicken with salt. Heat oil in large nonstick skillet over medium-high heat. Add chicken and cook, turning occasionally, until browned and cooked through, about 5 minutes. Transfer to plate.

2 Add bell pepper and scallions to skillet. Cook over medium heat, stirring frequently, until softened, about 3 minutes. Stir in curry paste and sugar; then coconut milk, cauliflower, and carrots. Bring to boil. Reduce heat and cover. Simmer, stirring occasionally, until vegetables are tender, about 6 minutes.

3 Return chicken to skillet and heat through. Stir in basil just before serving.

Per serving (375 ml [1½ cup]): 247 Cal, 11 g Total Fat, 1 g Sat Fat, 0 g Trans Fat, 47 mg Chol, 365 mg Sod, 20 g Carb, 7 g Sugar, 5 g Fib, 21 g Prot, 76 mg Calc.

stay on track

Cook a large batch of nutrient-rich brown rice on the weekend to serve with dishes during the week. Refrigerate cooked rice in an airtight container up to 4 days. A 125-ml (½-cup) portion of cooked brown rice has a ***PointsPlus*** value of ***3***.

thai red curry with chicken and vegetables

linguine puttanesca with chicken and artichokes

serves 6

per serving

- ▲ **225 g (½ lb) whole wheat linguine**
- **1 jar (500 ml [16 fl oz]) puttanesca sauce**
- ▲ **1 yellow squash, halved lengthwise and cut into 1.25-cm (½-in) slices**
- ▲ **1 can (398 ml [13 fl. oz]) water-packed quartered artichoke hearts, drained**
- **3 garlic cloves, minced**
- ▲ **375 ml (1½ cup) shredded cooked skinless chicken breast**
- **1 ml (¼ tsp) crushed red pepper flakes**

1 Cook linguine according to package directions, omitting salt.

2 Meanwhile, combine the puttanesca sauce, squash, artichoke hearts, and garlic in large saucepan; bring to simmer over medium heat. Reduce heat and cover. Cook just until squash is tender, about 10 minutes. Stir in chicken and pepper flakes. Serve sauce over linguine.

Per serving (125 ml [½ cup] linguine and 125 ml [½ cup] sauce): 282 Cal, 5 g Total Fat, 0 g Sat Fat, 0 g Trans Fat, 30 mg Chol, 899 Sod, 64 g Carb, 3 g Sugar, 13 g Fib, 31 g Prot, 79 mg Calc.

stay on track

Whole wheat pasta makes a nutritious and filling base for dinner. If this dish seems a little high in ***PointsPlus*** value, consider serving it with a ***0 PointsPlus*** value salad of baby spinach leaves and red bell pepper tossed with red-wine vinegar and seasoned salt.

chicken with israeli couscous salad

serves 4

per serving

- 500 ml (2 cups) water
- 250 ml (1 cup) Israeli couscous
- 2 ml (½ tsp) salt
- ▲ 1 small cucumber, peeled, seeded, and diced
- 45 ml (3 Tbsp) chopped fresh mint
- 10 ml (2 tsp) olive oil
- 5 ml (1 tsp) Italian seasoning
- ▲ 450 g (1 lb) skinless boneless chicken breast, cut into 3.75-cm (1½-in) pieces

1 To make salad, bring water to boil in medium saucepan. Add couscous and 1 ml (¼ tsp) salt. Reduce heat and cover. Simmer until couscous is tender, about 10 minutes; drain. Rinse under cold running water; drain and transfer to large bowl. Add cucumber, mint, oil, and 2 ml (½ tsp) of Italian seasoning; toss to combine.

2 Meanwhile, spray broiler rack with nonstick spray; preheat broiler.

3 Thread chicken onto 4 (25-cm [10-in]) metal skewers. Sprinkle kebabs with remaining 1 ml (¼ tsp) salt and remaining 2 ml (½ tsp) Italian seasoning. Spray kebabs with nonstick spray. Place on rack and broil 12.5 cm (5 in) from heat, turning frequently, until cooked through, about 8 minutes. Serve kebabs with salad.

Per serving (1 skewer and generous 175 ml (¾ cup) salad): 276 Cal, 5 g Total Fat, 1 g Sat Fat, 0 g Trans Fat, 63 mg Chol, 351 mg Sod, 28 g Carb, 1 g Sugar, 2 g Fib, 27 g Prot, 23 mg Calc.

for your information

Delicious and quick cooking, Israeli couscous consists of large beads of toasted pasta that resemble pearl barley. Look for it in larger supermarkets or specialty-foods stores.

moroccan couscous with chicken and dates

serves 4

10 PointsPlus® value per serving

- 30 ml (2 Tbsp) mango chutney
- 5 ml (1 tsp) Dijon mustard
- 1 ml (¼ tsp) salt
- 4 (85-g [3-oz]) skinless boneless chicken thighs
- ½ (198-g [7-oz]) box couscous
- 6 pitted dried dates, chopped
- 30 ml (2 Tbsp) chopped fresh cilantro
- ▲ 15 ml (1 Tbsp) finely chopped red onion

1 Combine chutney, mustard, and salt in medium bowl; add chicken and toss to coat. Set ridged grill pan over medium-high heat. Add chicken and cook, turning frequently, until chicken is cooked through, about 8 minutes.

2 Meanwhile, prepare couscous according to package directions, omitting butter or oil.

3 Fluff couscous with fork and transfer to platter. Top with chicken, dates, cilantro, and onion.

Per serving (1 chicken thigh and scant 125 ml [½ cup] couscous): 380 Cal, 8 g Total Fat, 2 g Sat Fat, 0 g Trans Fat, 56 mg Chol, 305 mg Sod, 62 g Carb, 30 g Sugar, 11 g Fib, 20 g Prot, 31 mg Calc.

creole oven-fried chicken

serves 4

per serving

- **60 ml (¼ cup) whole wheat panko (Japanese bread crumbs)**
- **30 ml (2 Tbsp) all-purpose flour**
- **15 ml (1 Tbsp) Creole seasoning**
- ▲ **150 ml (⅔ cup) fat-free buttermilk**
- **10 ml (2 tsp) Dijon mustard**
- **8 (100-g [3½-oz]) skinless chicken drumsticks**

1 Preheat oven to 230°C (450°F). Line broiler pan with foil.

2 Mix panko, flour, and Creole seasoning in large shallow bowl. Whisk buttermilk and mustard together in medium bowl. Dip drumsticks, one at a time, into buttermilk mixture, then roll in panko mixture to coat.

3 Lightly spray chicken with nonstick spray and place on broiler pan. Bake until crispy and cooked through, 20–25 minutes.

Per serving (2 drumsticks): 186 Cal, 4 g Total Fat, 1 g Sat Fat, 0 g Trans Fat, 86 mg Chol, 654 mg Sod, 10 g Carb, 2 g Sugar, 1 g Fib, 26 g Prot, 67 mg Calc.

grilled drumsticks with molasses barbecue sauce

grilled drumsticks with molasses barbecue sauce

serves 4

5 PointsPlus® value per serving

90 ml (6 Tbsp) ketchup
30 ml (2 Tbsp) molasses
30 ml (2 Tbsp) apple cider vinegar
12 ml (2½ tsp) chili powder
▲ **30 ml (2 Tbsp) minced onion**
3 garlic cloves, minced
8 (100-g [3½-oz]) skinless chicken drumsticks

1 To make barbecue sauce, combine ketchup, molasses, vinegar, chili powder, onion, and garlic in small saucepan; bring to boil. Reduce heat to low and simmer, stirring, 5 minutes.

2 Meanwhile, spray grill rack with nonstick spray. Preheat grill to medium or prepare a medium fire. Place chicken on grill rack and grill, turning occasionally, until browned, about 8 minutes. Brush with barbecue sauce. Cook, turning frequently, until chicken is glazed and cooked through, 5–6 minutes longer.

Per serving (2 drumsticks): 195 Cal, 4 g Total Fat, 1 g Sat Fat, 0 g Trans Fat, 86 mg Chol, 371 mg Sod, 15 g Carb, 11 g Sugar, 1 g Fib, 24 g Prot, 44 mg Calc.

stay on track

Serve these spicy drumsticks with steamed vegetable ribbons and brown rice. A 125-ml (½-cup) serving of cooked brown rice per person will increase the ***PointsPlus*** value by ***3***.

braised chicken thighs with feta and olives

serves 4

per serving

5 ml (1 tsp) olive oil

4 (115-g [¼-lb]) skinless boneless chicken thighs

▲ **125 ml (½ cup) reduced-sodium chicken broth**

▲ **2 plum tomatoes, chopped**

▲ **1 small onion, thinly sliced**

8 pitted brine-cured kalamata olives, chopped

45 ml (3 Tbsp) chopped fresh basil

▲ **60 ml (4 Tbsp) crumbled reduced fat feta cheese**

1 Heat oil in large skillet over medium-high heat. Add chicken and cook until lightly browned, about 3 minutes per side.

2 Add broth, tomatoes, onion, and olives; bring to boil. Reduce heat and cover. Simmer until vegetables are tender and chicken is cooked through, about 5 minutes. Remove skillet from heat and stir in basil. Serve sprinkled with feta.

Per serving (1 chicken thigh, 60 ml [¼ cup] sauce, and 15 ml [1 Tbsp] feta): 190 Cal, 7 g Total Fat, 2 g Sat Fat, 0 g Tran Fat, 110 mg Chol, 355 mg Sod, 4 g Carb, 2 g Sugar, 1 g Fib 24 g Prot, 57 mg Calc.

wild mushroom and sausage risotto

serves 4

per serving

- ▲ **1 carton (900 ml [32 fl. oz]) reduced-sodium chicken broth**
- **5 ml (1 tsp) olive oil**
- **225 g (½ lb) sun-dried tomato chicken sausage, casings removed, sausage diced**
- ▲ **1 (115-g [4-oz]) package sliced mixed wild mushrooms**
- **10 ml (2 tsp) chopped fresh thyme**
- **250 ml (1 cup) Arborio rice**
- **75 ml (⅓ cup) dry white wine**
- **30 ml (2 Tbsp) grated Parmesan cheese**
- **1 ml (¼ tsp) black pepper**

1 Bring broth to boil in medium saucepan. Reduce heat and keep at simmer.

2 Meanwhile, heat oil in large saucepan over medium-high heat. Add sausage and cook, stirring occasionally, until lightly browned, 3–4 minutes. Add mushrooms and thyme. Cook, stirring frequently, until mushrooms begin to soften, about 2 minutes. Stir in rice; reduce heat to medium and cook, stirring constantly, 1 minute. Add wine and cook, stirring constantly, until liquid is absorbed, about 1 minute.

3 Add broth, 125 ml (½ cup) at a time, stirring until broth is absorbed before adding more. Cook just until rice is tender, 18–20 minutes (you may have some broth leftover). Remove saucepan from heat and stir in Parmesan and pepper. Serve at once.

Per serving (250 ml [1 cup]): 345 Cal, 8 g Total Fat, 2 g Sat Fat, 0 g Trans Fat, 49 mg Chol, 428 mg Sod, 44 g Carb, 2 g Sugar, 2 g Fib, 20 g Prot, 44 mg Calc.

hearty kale and sausage soup

hearty kale and sausage soup

serves 4

per serving

- 5 ml (1 tsp) olive oil
- 225 g (½ lb) turkey kielbasa, sliced
- ▲ 500 ml (2 cups) reduced-sodium chickenbroth
- 500 ml (2 cups) water
- ▲ 500 g (1 lb) small red potatoes, diced
- ▲ 1 tomato, diced
- ▲ 1 onion, diced
- 5ml (1 tsp) smoked paprika
- ▲ 1 L (4 cups) sliced kale leaves

1 Heat oil in large saucepan over medium-high heat. Add kielbasa and cook, stirring occasionally, until lightly browned, 4–5 minutes; transfer to plate.

2 Add broth, water, potatoes, tomato, onion, and paprika; bring to boil. Cook until potatoes just soften, about 10 minutes.

3 Remove pan from heat and coarsely mash potatoes with wooden spoon. Stir in kale and return to boil. Reduce heat and cover. Simmer 5 minutes. Stir in kielbasa and cook until flavours are blended and kale is tender, about 5 minutes longer.

Per serving (375 ml [1½ cup]): 252 Cal, 8 g Total Fat, 2 g Sat Fat, 0 g Trans Fat, 35 mg Chol, 586 mg Sod, 33 g Carb, 5 g Sugar, 5 g Fib, 15 g Prot, 124 mg Calc.

stay on track

If you like you can make this soup even more filling by doubling the amount of tomato and kale; your portions will be about 75 ml (⅓ cup) larger and the ***PointsPlus*** value will remain the same.

hoisin duck wraps with spicy slaw

serves 4

per serving

- 60 ml (¼ cup) sake or sherry
- 30 ml (2 Tbsp) reduced-sodium soy sauce
- 1 ml (¼ tsp) Chinese five-spice powder
- 120 ml (8 Tbsp) hoisin sauce
- 30 ml (2 Tbsp) honey
- 1 skinless boneless duck breast (450-g [1-lb]), trimmed
- ▲ 1 L (4 cups) packaged coleslaw mix
- ▲ ½ Thai chile pepper, seeded and minced
- 30 ml (2 Tbsp) low-fat sesame-ginger dressing
- 4 (17.5-cm [7-in]) flour tortillas, warmed
- ▲ 1 cucumber, peeled, seeded, and cut lengthwise into thin strips
- ▲ 2 scallions, halved lengthwise

1 Preheat oven to 230°C (450°F). Line roasting pan with foil; place wire rack in pan and spray with nonstick spray.

2 Combine sake, soy sauce, five-spice powder, 75 ml (5 Tbsp) hoisin sauce, and 15 ml (1 Tbsp) honey in zip-close plastic bag; add duck. Squeeze out air and seal bag; turn to coat duck. Refrigerate, turning bag occasionally, 10 minutes or up to 1 day.

3 Combine remaining 45 ml (3 Tbsp) hoisin sauce and remaining 15 ml (1 Tbsp) honey in small bowl; set aside. Remove duck from marinade, discard marinade, and place duck on rack. Bake until cooked through, about 16 minutes. Remove duck from oven, cover loosely with foil, and let stand 5 minutes.

4 Combine coleslaw mix, chile, and dressing in medium bowl and toss. Thinly slice duck across grain. Spread one-fourth reserved hoisin mixture over each tortilla and top each with one-fourth cucumber, one-fourth duck, and 1 piece scallion. Roll up. Serve with slaw.

Per serving (1 wrap and 250 ml [1 cup] slaw): 339 Cal, 7 g Total Fat, 2 g Sat Fat, 0 g Trans Fat, 87 mg Chol, 702 mg Sod, 35 g Carb, 14 g Sugar, 3 g Fib, 27 g Prot, 65 mg Calc.

hoisin duck wraps with spicy slaw

wild salmon en papillote

serves 4

per serving

- ▲ **1 small seedless orange, peeled and chopped**
- ▲ **1 plum tomato, diced**
- **1 small shallot, finely chopped**
- **8 pitted niçiose olives (not cured in oil), chopped**
- **10 ml (2 tsp) capers, drained**
- ▲ **4 (115-g [¼-lb]) skinless wild salmon fillets**
- **1 ml (¼ tsp) salt**
- **1 ml (¼ tsp) black pepper**

1 Preheat oven to 200°C (400°F). Tear off 4 (30 x 35-cm [12 x 14-in]) sheets parchment paper. Fold each one in half lengthwise and cut into heart shape with the fold running vertically down centre. Open each heart and spray with nonstick spray.

2 In medium bowl, combine orange, tomato, shallot, olives, and capers. Sprinkle salmon with salt and pepper. Place 1 fillet onto centre of one side of each parchment heart. Top each fillet with about 75 ml (⅓ cup) orange mixture. Fold parchment over fish. Starting at top of each heart, crimp edges to seal packets. Place on baking sheet and bake until fillets are just opaque in centre, about 12 minutes.

3 Carefully open one side of each packet to let steam escape and slide contents onto a plate.

Per serving (1 packet): 212 Cal, 9 g Total Fat, 1 g Sat Fat, 0 g Trans Fat, 72 mg Chol, 330 mg Sod, 5 g Carb, 3 g Sugar, 1 g Fib, 26 g Prot, 33 mg Calc.

stay on track

If you have a choice between purchasing wild salmon and farm-raised salmon, consider opting for wild: Although farm-raised salmon is usually the cheaper option, it can be higher in some contaminants than wild salmon. And wild salmon, fresh or canned, is lower in fat content and a Power Food.

catfish escabèche with cilantro brown rice

serves 4

per serving

- 375 ml (1½ cup) water
- 2 ml (½ tsp) salt
- ▲ 375 ml (1½ cup) quick-cooking brown rice
- ▲ 4 (115-g [¼-lb]) skinless catfish fillets
- 5 ml (1 tsp) canola oil
- ▲ 2 bell peppers (any colours), cut into 5-cm (2-in) strips
- 3 garlic cloves, thinly sliced
- ▲ 1 (450-g [16-oz]) jar fat-free salsa
- 175 ml (¾ cup) orange juice
- Zest and juice of ½ lemon
- 45 ml (3 Tbsp) chopped fresh cilantro

1 Bring water and 1 ml (¼ tsp) of salt to boil in small saucepan. Stir in rice; reduce heat, cover, and simmer until rice is tender, about 10 minutes.

2 Sprinkle catfish with remaining 1 ml (¼ tsp) salt. Heat oil in large nonstick skillet over medium heat. Add the catfish and cook until just opaque in centre, 2–3 minutes per side. Transfer to plate.

3 Add bell peppers and garlic to skillet. Cook, stirring frequently, until bell peppers are crisp-tender, about 5 minutes. Stir in salsa, orange juice, and lemon zest and juice; bring to simmer. Cook, stirring occasionally, until bell peppers are just tender, about 5 minutes.

4 Return catfish to skillet and spoon vegetables and sauce over fillets. Cook until catfish is heated through, about 2 minutes longer. Toss rice with cilantro and serve with catfish and vegetables.

Per serving (1 fillet, 150 ml [⅔ cup] sauce, and 150 ml [⅔ cup] rice): 329 Cal, 8 g Total Fat, 2 g Sat Fat, 0 g Trans Fat, 51 mg Chol, 776 mg Sod, 41 g Carb, 5 g Sugar, 3 g Fib, 21 g Prot, 37 mg Calc.

garlicky spaghetti with shrimp and white beans

garlicky spaghetti with shrimp and white beans

serves 4

per serving

- ▲ 115 g (¼ lb) whole wheat spaghetti
- 10 ml (2 tsp) olive oil
- ▲ 1 onion, finely chopped
- 5 garlic cloves, sliced
- ▲ 250 ml (1 cup) rinsed and drained canned white beans
- ▲ 450 g (1 lb) large peeled and deveined shrimp
- ▲ 250 ml (1 cup) reduced-sodium chicken broth
- 15 ml (1 Tbsp) lemon juice
- 1 ml (¼ tsp) red pepper flakes
- 60 ml (¼ cup) fresh basil leaves, thinly sliced

1 Cook pasta according to package directions, omitting salt. Drain.

2 Meanwhile, heat oil in large skillet over medium heat. Add onion; cover and cook until onion is translucent, about 5 minutes. Add garlic and cook until fragrant, about 30 seconds. Stir in beans, shrimp, broth, lemon juice, and pepper flakes. Cover and bring to boil. Reduce heat and simmer, covered, until shrimp are just opaque in centre, 3–4 minutes.

3 Toss shrimp mixture with pasta and sprinkle with basil.

Per serving (375 ml [1½ cup]): 334 Cal, 5 g Total Fat, 1 g Sat Fat, 0 g Trans Fat, 221 mg Chol, 280 mg Sod, 41 g Carb, 4 g Sugar, 8 g Fib, 34 g Prot, 128 mg Calc.

stay on track

Flavouring dishes like this one with a combination of herbs and lemon can go a long way in satisfying your taste buds while keeping the fat and sodium levels in your dishes down. Try herbs and lemon on other pasta dishes, in tuna or salmon salads, over rice, or on steamed vegetables.

broiled lobster tails with mango salsa

serves 4

per serving

- 1 large lime
- ▲ 250 ml (1 cup) diced peeled seeded mango
- ▲ ½ red bell pepper, diced
- ▲ ½ jalapeño pepper, seeded and finely diced
- 30 ml (2 Tbsp) chopped fresh cilantro
- 2 ml (½ tsp) salt
- ▲ 4 (115-g [¼-lb]) frozen lobster tails, thawed
- 5 ml (1 tsp) olive oil

1 Grate 5 ml (1 tsp) of zest and squeeze 30 ml (2 Tbsp) of juice from lime. Combine lime zest and juice in large bowl and stir in mango, bell pepper, jalapeño, cilantro, and 1 ml (¼ tsp) of salt.

2 Spray broiler rack with nonstick spray; preheat broiler. Using kitchen shears, cut through shell lengthwise on top and bottom of each lobster tail. Grasp sides of shell of 1 tail and press down so meat pops up; repeat with remaining tails.

3 Place tails on broiler rack, top side up. Drizzle lobster with oil and sprinkle with remaining 1 ml (¼ tsp) salt. Broil tails 15 cm (6 in) from heat until just opaque in centre, 5–6 minutes. Serve at once with salsa.

Per serving (1 lobster tail and 75 ml [⅓ cup] salsa): 152 Cal, 2 g Total Fat, 0 g Sat Fat, 0 g Trans Fat, 81 mg Chol, 724 mg Sod, 10 g Carb, 7 g Sugar, 1 g Fib, 23 g Prot, 88 mg Calc.

ancho chili verde with tempeh

serves 4

per serving

- 250 ml (1 cup) water
- 1 ml (¼ tsp) salt
- ▲ 250 ml (1 cup) quick-cooking brown rice
- 5 ml (1 tsp) canola oil
- 340 g (¾ lb) tempeh, diced (about 500 ml [2 cups])
- 3 garlic cloves, finely chopped
- ▲ 2 poblano peppers, coarsely chopped
- 10 ml (2 tsp) ancho chili powder
- 10 ml (2 tsp) ground cumin
- ▲ 1 jar fat-free (450-g [16-oz]) salsa verde
- ▲ 125 ml (½ cup) low-sodium vegetable broth

1 Bring water and salt to boil in small saucepan. Stir in rice; reduce heat, cover, and simmer until rice is tender, about 10 minutes.

2 Meanwhile, heat oil in large skillet over medium-high heat. Add tempeh and garlic. Cook, stirring occasionally, until tempeh is lightly browned, about 3 minutes.

3 Stir in poblanos, chili powder, and cumin. Cook, stirring frequently, until poblanos are crisp-tender, about 2 minutes. Stir in salsa and broth; bring to boil. Reduce heat and simmer until poblanos are tender, about 10 minutes.

4 Divide rice among 4 bowls and top evenly with chili.

Per serving (125 ml [½ cup] rice and 250 ml [1 cup] chili): 334 Cal, 12 g Total Fat, 2 g Sat Fat, 0 g Trans Fat, 0 mg Chol, 632 mg Sod, 39 g Carb, 4 g Sugar, 4 g Fib, 19 g Prot, 119 mg Calc.

for your information

Looking for more meatless protein options to work into your diet? Tempeh (TEHM-pay) is a fermented soybean cake with a delicious nutty flavour and firm, meatlike texture. Look for it in the refrigerated section of supermarkets or natural foods stores.

cold noodles with tofu and spicy peanut sauce

serves 4

per serving

- ▲ **115 g (4 oz) whole wheat linguine or spaghetti**
- **45 ml (3 Tbsp) reduced-fat smooth peanut butter**
- **30 ml (2 Tbsp) rice vinegar**
- **30 ml (2 Tbsp) reduced-sodium soy sauce**
- **5 ml (1 tsp) sugar**
- **1 ml (¼ tsp) red pepper flakes, or to taste**
- ▲ **395 g (14 oz) packaged firm silken tofu, drained and diced**
- ▲ **1 red bell pepper, cut into thin strips**
- ▲ **1 Kirby (pickling) cucumber, peeled, seeded, and diced**
- ▲ **3 scallions, chopped**
- **30 ml (2 Tbsp) chopped dry-roasted peanuts**

1 Cook linguine according to package directions, omitting salt. Drain; rinse under cold running water and drain again.

2 Meanwhile, whisk together peanut butter, vinegar, soy sauce, sugar, and pepper flakes in small bowl. (Whisk in 15 ml (1 Tbsp) water if the mixture is too thick to pour easily.)

3 Combine linguine, tofu, bell pepper, cucumber, and scallions in large bowl. Add peanut sauce and toss to coat. Sprinkle with peanuts.

Per serving (310 ml [1¼ cups] noodles and 7 ml [½ Tbsp] peanuts): 286 Cal, 11 g Total Fat, 2 g Sat Fat, 0 g Trans Fat, 0 mg Chol, 424 mg Sod, 35 g Carb, 6 g Sugar, 6 g Fib, 14 g Prot, 96 mg Calc.

for your information

You can make this salad ahead and store it in a covered container in the refrigerator up to 2 days. It makes a great brown-bag lunch.

cold noodles with tofu and spicy peanut sauce

sicilian-style penne with eggplant

serves 4

per serving

- ▲ 225 g (½ lb) whole wheat penne
- ▲ 10 sun-dried tomato halves (not packed in oil), coarsely chopped
- 15 ml (1 Tbsp) olive oil
- ▲ 340 g (¾ lb) eggplant, cut into 3.75-cm (1½-in) cubes
- 30 ml (2 Tbsp) balsamic vinegar
- 125 ml (½ cup) chopped fresh basil
- 60 ml (4 Tbsp) crumbled ricotta salata cheese

1 Cook penne according to package directions, omitting salt.

2 Meanwhile, place tomatoes in small bowl and cover with boiling water. Let soak 5 minutes. Drain and coarsely chop.

3 Heat oil in large skillet over medium-high heat. Add eggplant and cook, turning frequently, until tender, about 6 minutes. Add tomatoes, vinegar, basil, and penne. Reduce heat to low and cook just until heated through. Serve with ricotta salata sprinkled over top.

Per serving (375 ml [1½ cup] pasta and sauce and 15 ml [1 Tbsp] cheese): 324 Cal, 8 g Total Fat, 3 g Sat Fat, 0 g Trans Fat, 0 mg Chol, 359 mg Sod, 52 g Carb, 7 g Sugar, 9 g Fib, 11 g Prot, 65 mg Calc.

for your information

Ricotta salata is a traditional Sicilian cheese made from pressed, dried ricotta cheese. If you like, you can substitute crumbled goat cheese for no change in ***PointsPlus*** value.

polenta and kale gratin

serves 4

per serving

- ▲ **1 carton (900 ml [32 fl. oz]) reduced-sodium chicken broth**
- ▲ **250 ml (1 cup) instant polenta**
- **250 ml (1 cup) part-skim ricotta cheese**
- ▲ **1 large egg**
- **5 ml (1 tsp) olive oil**
- ▲ **225 g (½ lb) baby kale**
- **2 garlic cloves, minced**
- **0.5 ml (⅛ tsp) salt**
- **125 ml (½ cup) shredded unsalted reduced-fat mozzarella cheese**

1 Preheat oven to 220°C (425°F). Spray 17.5 x 28-5 cm (7 x 11-in) baking dish with nonstick spray.

2 Bring broth to boil in medium saucepan over medium-high heat. Gradually sprinkle polenta into saucepan, beating constantly with whisk. Reduce heat and cook, continuing to beat, until thick and creamy, 3–4 minutes. Remove saucepan from heat. Beat in ricotta and egg. Spoon polenta mixture into prepared baking dish.

3 Heat oil in large skillet over medium heat. Add kale, garlic, and salt. Cook, stirring occasionally, until kale wilts, about 5 minutes (stir in water, 15 ml [1 Tbsp] at a time, if kale begins to stick to bottom of skillet). Spoon kale evenly over polenta mixture and sprinkle with mozzarella cheese. Bake until cheese is melted and lightly browned, about 15 minutes.

Per serving (375 ml [1½ cup]): 345 Cal, 11 g Total Fat, 5 g Sat Fat, 0 g Trans Fat, 80 mg Chol, 359 mg Sod, 40 g Carb, 1 g Sugar, 3 g Fib, 22 g Prot, 462 mg Calc.

YOUR SNACKS AND SWEETS

—

for ***5 PointsPlus*** value or less

snacks

Shrimp Cocktail Salads
Spicy Halibut Ceviche in Endive
Savoury Tomato Bites
Smoked Trout Dip with Dill and Horseradish
Chips with Avocado Salsa
Black Bean–Queso Dip
Andouille Corn Bread
Spinach and Sausage Snack Rolls
Onion and Fontina Phyllo Squares
Curried Vegetable Fritters
Italian Fennel-and-Sausage Mushrooms
Chili-Garlic Edamame
Fruit and Spice Popcorn Mix

desserts

Five-Spice Carrot Cake
Cranberry Tea Scones
Spiced Pumpkin-Mango Loaf
Walnut-Crunch Bran Muffins
Dark Chocolate Soufflés with Raspberry Sauce
Honey Rice Pudding with Fruit
Chocolate Turtle Ice-Cream Cake
Gingersnap Ice-Cream Sandwiches
Mocha Malts
Pineapple Foster with Yogourt
Baked Apples with Ricotta
Strawberries with Caramel Fondue
Mocha-Walnut Biscotti
Clementine Madeleines
Heavenly Oat Bars
Cantaloupe-Lime Frosty
Chilled Honeydew-Mint Soup

shrimp cocktail salads

under 20 minutes • serves 2

per serving

- 15 ml (1 Tbsp) lime juice
- 5 ml (1 tsp) honey
- 5 ml (1 tsp) olive oil
- 1 ml (¼ tsp) ground cumin
- 0.5 ml (⅛ tsp) salt
- Pinch cayenne
- ▲ 115 g (¼ lb) large peeled cooked shrimp (about 8)
- ▲ ½ small jicama, peeled and cut into 8 chunks
- ▲ 4 cherry tomatoes, halved
- 15 ml (1 Tbsp) chopped fresh cilantro
- ▲ 375 ml (1½ cups) mixed baby salad greens

1 Whisk together lime juice, honey, oil, cumin, salt, and cayenne in medium bowl. Add shrimp, jicama, tomatoes, and cilantro and toss to coat.

2 Thread 2 shrimp, 2 pieces jicama, and 2 tomato halves on each of 4 (15 cm [6 in]) wooden skewers. Reserve any dressing remaining in bowl. Divide greens between 2 plates; place 2 kebabs on each plate. Drizzle evenly with reserved dressing.

Per serving (2 skewers and 175 ml [¾ cup] greens): 138 Cal, 3 g Total Fat, 1 g Sat Fat, 0 g Trans Fat, 111 mg Chol, 294 mg Sod, 15 g Carb, 7 g Sugar, 6 g Fib, 13 g Prot, 40 mg Calc.

for your information

You can save time by skipping the skewers—just serve the shrimp and vegetable mixture over the greens.

shrimp cocktail salads

spicy halibut ceviche in endive

under 20 minutes • serves 2

per serving

- ▲ **(225 g [½ lb]) very fresh skinless halibut fillets, cut into 0.6-cm (¼-in) dice**
- **60 ml (¼ cup) lime juice**
- ▲ **8 grape tomatoes, chopped**
- ▲ **1 small seedless orange, peeled and diced**
- ▲ **45 ml (3 Tbsp) diced red onion**
- ▲ **5 ml (1 tsp) seeded, diced jalapeño pepper, or to taste**
- **1 small clove garlic, minced**
- **1 ml (¼ tsp) salt**
- **30 ml (2 Tbsp) chopped fresh cilantro**
- ▲ **8 Belgian endive leaves**

1 Combine halibut and lime juice in medium bowl; toss to coat. Let stand 5 minutes.

2 Add tomatoes, orange, onion, jalapeño, garlic, and salt to bowl and toss to combine. Cover and refrigerate about 10 minutes.

3 Add cilantro and toss to combine. Evenly spoon ceviche into endive leaves and serve at once.

Per serving **(4 filled endive leaves): 195 Cal, 3 g Total Fat, 0 g Sat Fat, 0 g Trans Fat, 36 mg Chol, 386 mg Sod, 17 g Carb, 7 g Sugar, 6 g Fib, 27 g Prot, 152 mg Calc.**

savoury tomato bites

under 20 minutes • serves 2

per serving

- ▲ **4 small plum tomatoes**
- ▲ **150 ml (2/3 cup) fat-free cottage cheese**
- ▲ **15 ml (1 Tbsp) minced red bell pepper**
- ▲ **15 ml (1 Tbsp) minced scallion**
- **15 ml (1 Tbsp) chopped fresh parsley or basil**
- **5 ml (1 tsp) grated lemon zest**
- **1 ml (1/4 tsp) salt**
- **0.5 ml (1/8 tsp) black pepper**

1 Halve tomatoes lengthwise. Using your fingers, pull out and discard seeds. With spoon or melon baller, scoop out flesh and place in medium bowl.

2 Add remaining ingredients to bowl and stir until combined. Spoon mixture into tomato halves, mounding to fill. Serve at once, or refrigerate up to 4 hours.

Per serving **(4 stuffed tomato halves): 80 Cal, 0 g Total Fat, 0 g Sat Fat, 0 g Trans Fat, 3 mg Chol, 585 mg Sod, 10 g Carb, 7 g Sugar, 2 g Fib, 10 g Prot, 60 mg Calc.**

stay on track

Looking for a light snack to hold you over until dinner? The combination of fibre-rich vegetables and protein-packed dairy makes this a very tasty and satisfying mid-afternoon treat. Enjoy them with a tall glass of seltzer with lime.

From top clockwise: smoked trout dip with dill and horseradish; savoury tomato bites, page 189; spicy halibut ceviche in endive, page 188

smoked trout dip with dill and horseradish

under 20 minutes • serves 6

per serving

- ▲ **1 container (500 ml [8 fl. oz]) fat-free sour cream**
- **15 ml (1 Tbsp) chopped fresh dill**
- **7 ml (1½ tsp) prepared horseradish**
- **5 ml (1 tsp) lemon juice**
- **0.5 ml (⅛ tsp) black pepper**
- **115 g (¼ lb) skinless smoked trout fillets, chopped**

Put sour cream, dill, horseradish, lemon juice, pepper, and half of trout in food processor or blender. Pulse just until combined. Transfer to small bowl; stir in remaining trout. Serve at once, or cover and refrigerate up to 3 days.

Per serving (60 ml [¼ cup]): 64 Cal, 1 g Total Fat, 0 g Sat Fat, 0 g Trans Fat, 18 mg Chol, 63 mg Sod, 6 g Carb, 0 g Sugar, 0 g Fib, 7 g Prot, 49 mg Calc.

stay on track

Crunchy vegetables are the perfect ***0 PointsPlus*** value accompaniment to this zesty dip. Cut up your favourites: Cucumbers are a classic with trout, and cauliflower florets and bell pepper strips are delicious, too.

chips with avocado salsa

under 20 minutes • serves 6

per serving

- **1 avocado, halved, pitted, peeled, and diced**
- ▲ **1 scallions, thinly sliced**
- ▲ **75 ml (⅓ cup) prepared fat-free salsa**
- ▲ **¼ English (seedless) cucumber, diced**
- **15 ml (1 Tbsp) chopped fresh cilantro**
- **10 ml (2 tsp) lime juice**
- **1 ml (¼ tsp) salt**
- **36 baked low-fat tortilla chips**

Put avocado, scallion, salsa, cucumber, cilantro, lime juice, and salt in medium bowl. Toss to combine. Serve at once, or cover and refrigerate up to 8 hours. Serve with chips.

Per serving (75 ml [⅓ cup] salsa with 6 chips): 89 Cal, 5 g Total Fat, 1 g Sat Fat, 0 g Trans Fat, 0 mg Chol, 247 mg Sod, 10 g Carb, 1 g Sugar, 2 g Fib, 1 g Prot, 21 mg Calc.

black bean–queso dip

under 20 minutes • serves 6

per serving

- ▲ **1 can (398 ml [15 fl. oz]) reduced-sodium black beans, rinsed and drained**
- ▲ **150 ml (2/3 cup) fat-free chunky salsa**
- **2 ml (1/2tsp) ground cumin**
- **250 ml (1 cup) shredded reduced-fat Mexican cheese blend**
- ▲ **2 scallions, thinly sliced**
- **750 ml (3 cups) baked low-fat tortilla chips**

1 Combine beans, salsa, and cumin in medium saucepan; set over medium heat. Cook, stirring occasionally, until heated through, about 3 minutes. Add Mexican cheese blend and cook, stirring constantly, until cheese is melted, about 2 minutes. Stir in scallions.

2 Transfer to fondue pot or bowl. Serve warm with tortilla chips.

Per serving (75 ml [1/3 cup] dip with about 125 ml [1/2 cup] chips): 145 Cal, 5 g Total Fat, 3 g Sat Fat, 0 g Trans Fat, 10 mg Chol, 497 mg Sod, 19 g Carb, 2 g Sugar, 4 g Fib, 8 g Prot, 308 mg Calc.

stay on track

Turn to this snack anytime you want a rich and creamy treat. Add some veggie dippers like carrot or fennel sticks for more crunch and no additional ***PointsPlus*** value.

andouille corn bread

serves 10

per serving

- 310 ml (1¼ cups) all-purpose flour
- ▲ 175 ml (¾ cup) yellow cornmeal
- 15 ml (1 Tbsp) sugar
- 7 ml (1½ tsp) baking powder
- 2 ml (½ tsp) baking soda
- 2 ml (½ tsp) salt
- 250 ml (1 cup) low-fat buttermilk
- 125 ml (½ cup) canned cream-style corn
- 30 ml (2 Tbsp) canola oil
- ▲ 1 large egg
- 85 g (3 oz) andouille sausage (about 1 sausage), diced

1 Preheat oven to 180°C (350°F). Spray 22.5 cm (9 in) round cake pan with nonstick spray.

2 Combine flour, cornmeal, sugar, baking powder, baking soda, and salt in large bowl. Whisk together buttermilk, corn, oil, and egg in medium bowl. Add buttermilk mixture to flour mixture and stir just until combined. Stir in sausage.

3 Spoon batter into prepared pan. Bake until toothpick inserted into centre of bread comes out with just a few moist crumbs attached, 20–25 minutes. Cut into 10 wedges.

Per serving (1 wedge): 175 Cal, 5 g Total Fat, 1 g Sat Fat, 0 g Trans Fat, 27 mg Chol, 399 mg Sod, 26 g Carb, 3 g Sugar, 1 g Fib, 5 g Prot, 48 mg Calc.

for your information

This flavourful bread is great to have on hand when you're craving a savoury snack or want something different to go with a light bowl of soup. Leftovers will stay fresh for 2 days refrigerated, or you can freeze the wedges wrapped in foil for up to 2 months.

spinach and sausage snack rolls

serves 8

per serving

- 5 ml (1 tsp) olive oil
- 225 ml (½ lb) Italian-style turkey sausage, casings removed
- ▲ 1 small red bell pepper, chopped
- ▲ 1 (300 g [10.5 oz]) package frozen leaf spinach, thawed and squeezed dry
- ▲ 1 large egg, lightly beaten
- 8 (35 x 45-cm [14 x 18-in]) sheets frozen phyllo dough, thawed

1 Preheat oven to 190°C (375°F). Spray baking sheet with nonstick spray; set aside.

2 Heat oil in large nonstick skillet over medium-high heat. Add sausage and bell pepper and cook, breaking up sausage with wooden spoon, until sausage is browned, about 10 minutes. Remove from heat. Stir in spinach and then egg.

3 Place 1 phyllo sheet on dry work surface. (Cover remaining dough with plastic wrap to keep it moist.) Spray lightly with nonstick spray. Put second sheet on top of first and spray lightly with nonstick spray. Fold the layered sheets in half, making a 35 x 22.5-cm (14 x 9-in) rectangle. Spread one-fourth of sausage mixture over rectangle and roll up from one narrow end. Place seam side down on baking sheet and spray lightly with nonstick spray. Repeat with remaining phyllo and filling, making 4 rolls.

4 Bake until crisp and golden brown, 20–25 minutes. Let cool 5 minutes, then cut in half and serve.

Per serving (½ roll): 181 Cal, 6 g Total Fat, 1 g Sat Fat, 0 g Trans Fat, 44 mg Chol, 309 mg Sod, 13 g Carb, 1 g Sugar, 2 g Fib, 8 g Prot, 51 mg Calc.

onion and fontina phyllo squares

serves 4

per serving

- 5 ml (1 tsp) olive oil
- ▲ 2 large (340-g [¾-lb]) Vidalia or other sweet onions, thinly sliced
- 60 ml (¼ cup) water
- 1 ml (¼ tsp) salt
- 8 niçoise or other small black olives, pitted and chopped
- 10 ml (2 tsp) chopped fresh thyme
- 2 ml (½ tsp) black pepper
- 8 sheets (35 x 45 cm [14 x 18 in]) frozen phyllo dough, thawed
- 60 ml (¼ cup) shredded fontina cheese

1 Heat oil in large nonstick skillet over medium-high heat. Add onions, water, and salt; bring to boil. Reduce heat and cover. Simmer, stirring occasionally, until onion is very soft, about 20 minutes. Remove from heat; pour off any excess water. Stir in olives, thyme, and pepper. Cool slightly.

2 Preheat oven to 200°C (400°F). Line baking sheet with parchment paper.

3 Place 1 phyllo sheet on dry work surface. (Cover remaining dough with plastic wrap to keep it moist.) Spray sheet lightly with nonstick spray. Put second sheet on top of first and spray lightly. Repeat until all 4 sheets are layered. Cut into 2 rectangles and stack rectangles on top of each other. Roll in edges of phyllo to make rimmed edge. Place on baking sheet.

4 Spread onion mixture evenly over phyllo. Bake until edges are golden brown, about 20 minutes. Sprinkle with fontina cheese and bake until cheese melts, about 5 minutes. Cut into 4 squares.

Per serving **(1 square): 112 Cal, 5 g Total Fat, 2 g Sat Fat, 0 g Trans Fat, 8 mg Chol, 349 mg Sod, 13 g Carb, 1 g Sugar, 1 g Fib, 3 g Prot, 54 mg Calc.**

onion and fontina
phyllo squares

curried vegetable fritters

serves 4

per serving

- ▲ **2 small 115 g (¼ lb) each new potatoes, peeled**
- ▲ **2 small zucchini**
- ▲ **2 small carrots, shredded**
- ▲ **2 scallions, finely chopped**
- ▲ **2 large egg whites, lightly beaten**
- **30 ml (2 Tbsp) all-purpose flour**
- **5 ml (1 tsp) curry powder**
- **2 ml (½ tsp) salt**
- **2 ml (½ tsp) black pepper**
- **10 ml (2 tsp) canola oil**

1 Place potatoes in small saucepan, add water to cover, and bring to boil. Reduce heat and simmer just until potatoes are tender, 6–8 minutes. Drain and cover with cold water to cool.

2 Meanwhile, coarsely shred zucchini onto double layer of paper towels. Spread out zucchini and let stand 3 minutes to drain. Combine zucchini, carrots, scallions, egg whites, flour, curry powder, salt, and pepper in large bowl. Drain potatoes, pat dry, and grate coarsely. Add to zucchini mixture.

3 Heat 5 ml (1 tsp) oil on large nonstick griddle or in large nonstick skillet over medium-high heat. Drop batter by 60-ml (¼-cup) measures onto griddle. Cook until golden, about 3 minutes per side. Repeat with remaining oil and batter to make total of 12 fritters.

Per serving **(3 fritters): 113 Cal, 3 g Total Fat, 0 g Sat Fat, 0 g Trans Fat, 0 mg Chol, 345 mg Sod, 19 g Carb, 3 g Sugar, 3 g Fib, 4 g Prot, 32 mg Calc.**

italian fennel-and-sausage mushrooms

serves 2

4 PointsPlus® value per serving

115 g (¼ lb) sweet Italian-style turkey sausage, casings removed

▲ 60 ml (¼ cup) finely chopped fennel bulb

30 ml (2 Tbsp) seasoned dried bread crumbs

▲ 2 (10 cm [4 in]) Portobello mushroom caps

15 ml (1 Tbsp) grated Asiago or Parmesan cheese

1 Preheat oven to 220°C (425°F). Spray baking sheet with nonstick spray.

2 Combine sausage, fennel, and bread crumbs in medium bowl. Spoon sausage mixture into each mushroom cap, mounding to fill. Sprinkle with Asiago; spray lightly with nonstick spray.

3 Place mushrooms on prepared baking sheet and cover loosely with foil. Bake 15 minutes. Remove foil and bake until mushrooms are browned and cooked through, about 5 minutes longer.

Per serving (1 stuffed mushroom): 161 Cal, 8 g Total Fat, 1 g Sat Fat, 0 g Trans Fat, 37 mg Chol, 526 mg Sod, 11 g Carb, 3 g Sugar, 2 g Fib, 13 g Prot, 47 mg Calc.

stay on track

Turn these mushrooms into a light lunch for two by serving them alongside a quick salad. Toss together mixed baby salad greens, halved cherry tomatoes, sliced cucumber, red-wine vinegar, and salt and black pepper to taste.

chili-garlic edamame

under 20 minutes • serves 2

per serving

- **2 ml (½ tsp) canola oil**
- **2 ml (½ tsp) grated peeled fresh ginger**
- **2 ml (½ tsp) chili-garlic paste, or to taste**
- ▲ **140 g (5 oz) frozen shelled edamame, thawed**
- **Pinch salt**

Heat oil in medium skillet over medium-high heat. Add ginger and chili-garlic paste. Cook, stirring frequently, until fragrant, about 30 seconds. Add edamame and salt. Cook, stirring, until heated through, about 4 minutes.

Per serving (about 150 ml [⅔ cup]): 89 Cal, 5 g Total Fat, 0 g Sat Fat, 0 g Trans Fat, 0 mg Chol, 106 mg Sod, 6 g Carb, 2 g Sugar, 3 g Fib, 7 g Prot, 43 mg Calc.

fruit and spice popcorn mix

under 20 minutes • serves 6

per serving

- 15 ml (1 Tbsp) olive oil
- 10 ml (2 tsp) paprika
- Pinch cayenne
- ▲ 1.5 L (6 cups) plain air-popped popcorn
- 175 ml (¾ cup) chopped mixed dried fruit
- 1 ml (¼ tsp) salt

1 Combine oil, paprika, and cayenne in microwavable cup. Microwave on High until fragrant, 45–60 seconds, stopping and stirring about every 15 seconds.

2 Stir together popcorn and dried fruit in large bowl. Drizzle spice mixture over popcorn mixture and toss gently to coat. Sprinkle with salt and toss again.

Per serving (250 ml [1 cup]): 113 Cal, 3 g Total Fat, 0 g Sat Fat, 0 g Trans Fat, 0 mg Chol, 126 mg Sod, 21 g Carb, 12 g Sugar, 2 g Fib, 2 g Prot, 12 mg Calc.

for your information

Store this snack mix in an airtight container at room temperature up to 1 week. It's great to have on hand when you need a crunchy afternoon treat.

satisfy your cravings

Got a hankering for something crunchy, sweet, spicy, cheesy, creamy, or savoury? We've got good news: There's no reason to say no to the flavours and textures you love. There are plenty of smart, satisfying treats that will hit the spot without toppling your eating plan. Try one of our healthy recipes listed here, or get almost-instant gratification with one of our Five-Minute Fixes.

Note: All ***PointsPlus*** values for the Five-Minute Fixes were calculated by adding the individual ***PointsPlus*** values for each ingredient.

In the Book

Crunchy

- **Chips with Avocado Salsa**, p 192, ***PointsPlus*** value ***2***
- **Mocha-Walnut Biscotti**, p 219, ***PointsPlus*** value ***2***

Sweet

- **Ginger Ice-Cream Sandwiches**, p 213, ***PointsPlus*** value ***3***
- **Five-Spice Carrot Cake**, p 204, ***PointsPlus*** value ***5***

Spicy

- **Chili-Garlic Edamame**, p 200, ***PointsPlus*** value ***2***
- **Spicy Halibut Ceviche in Endive**, p 188, ***PointsPlus*** value ***5***

Cheesy

- **Black Bean–Queso Dip**, p 193, ***PointsPlus*** value ***4***
- **Onion and Fontina Phyllo Squares**, p 196, ***PointsPlus*** value ***3***

Creamy

- **Strawberries with Caramel Fondue**, p 218, ***PointsPlus*** value ***3***
- **Honey Rice Pudding with Fruit**, p 211, ***PointsPlus*** value ***5***

Savoury

- **Smoked Trout Dip with Dill and Horseradish**, p 191, ***PointsPlus*** value ***2***
- **Italian Fennel-and-Sausage Mushrooms**, p 199, ***PointsPlus*** value ***4***

Five-Minute Fixes

Crunchy

- **Crunchy Banana Pops**
Cut 1 banana in half and insert popsicle sticks into cut ends. Roll banana in 125 ml (½ cup) crushed honey-nut cereal. ***PointsPlus*** value ***2***

- **Cheesy Popcorn**
Toss 750 ml (3 cups) air-popped popcorn with 30 ml (2 Tbsp) grated Parmesan and 1 ml (¼ tsp) each salt and black pepper. ***PointsPlus*** value ***3***

- **Crispy PB&Js**
Top 2 multi-grain rice cakes with 10 ml (2 tsp) peanut butter and 10 ml (2 tsp) jam. ***PointsPlus*** value ***5***

Sweet

- **Raspberry-Ricotta Parfait**
Top 125 ml (½ cup) fresh raspberries with 60 ml (¼ cup) part-skim ricotta. Drizzle with 5 ml (1 tsp) honey. ***PointsPlus*** value ***3***

- **Chocolate-Cherry Cooler**
Blend 250 ml (1 cup) unsweetened almond milk, 10 unsweetened frozen pitted cherries (75 ml [⅓ cup]), and 1 packet fat-free cocoa mix until smooth. ***PointsPlus*** value ***2***

Spicy

- **Crudités with Spiced Hummus**
Mix 30 ml (2 Tbsp) hummus with 1 ml (¼ tsp) cayenne. Serve with 250 ml (1 cup) carrot sticks. ***PointsPlus*** value ***2***

- **Spicy Pita Wedges**
Toast 1 small whole wheat pita; slice into wedges. Mix 60 ml (¼ cup) each diced avocado and hot salsa. Serve with pita. ***PointsPlus*** value ***4***

- **Devil's Almonds**
Sprinkle 23 almonds with a pinch each cayenne and paprika. ***PointsPlus*** value ***5***

Cheesy

- **Apple "Cheesecake"**
Top 1 sliced medium apple with 1 wedge light spreadable cheese. Sprinkle with 1 ml (¼ tsp) cinnamon. ***PointsPlus*** value ***1***

- **Pimiento Cheese Canapés**
Mix 125 ml (½ cup) fat-free cream cheese, 15 ml (1 Tbsp) chopped pimiento, and 15 ml (1 Tbsp) chopped fresh basil. Spoon onto 8 cucumber rounds. ***PointsPlus*** value ***3***

Creamy

- **Banana-Peanut Butter Freeze**
In a food processor, puree 1 sliced frozen banana, 15 ml (1 Tbsp) skim milk, 7 ml (½ Tbsp) peanut butter, and 1 ml (¼ tsp) cinnamon. ***PointsPlus*** value ***1***

- **Chocolate "Pudding"**
Combine ½ packet no-sugar-added cocoa mix with 170 g (6 oz) plain fat-free Greek yogourt; stir until smooth. ***PointsPlus*** value ***3***

- **Tofu-Berry Smoothie**
Blend together 55 g (2 oz) silken tofu, 125 ml (½ cup) unsweetened frozen blueberries, ⅓ banana, and 175 ml (¾ cup) skim milk. ***PointsPlus*** value ***3***

Savoury

- **Tomato-Cheddar Soup**
Stir 60 ml (¼ cup) shredded low-fat Cheddar cheese into 125 ml (½ cup) hot canned tomato soup prepared with water. Sprinkle with black pepper. ***PointsPlus*** value ***2***

- **Mexican Egg Wrap**
Scramble 1 large egg in a nonstick pan with pinch each salt and chili powder. Serve in a warmed small corn tortilla. ***PointsPlus*** value ***3***

five-spice carrot cake

serves 12

per serving

- 375 ml (1½ cups) cake flour (not self-rising)
- 7 ml (1½ tsp) baking powder
- 5 ml (1 tsp) five-spice powder
- 2 ml (½ tsp) baking soda
- 2 ml (½ tsp) salt
- 175 ml (¾ cup) granulated sugar
- ▲ 1 large egg
- ▲ 1 large egg white
- 30 ml (2 Tbsp) canola oil
- 10 ml (2 tsp) grated peeled fresh ginger
- ▲ 225 g (8 oz) canned crushed pineapple in juice, drained, 60 ml (¼ cup) of juice reserved
- ▲ 2 carrots, shredded
- 60 ml (¼ cup) raisins
- 115 g (¼ lb) fat-free cream cheese
- 60 ml (¼ cup) confectioners' sugar
- 15 ml (1 Tbsp) low-fat (1%) milk

1 Preheat oven to 180°C (350°F). Spray 20 cm (8-in) square baking pan with nonstick spray.

2 Sift flour, baking powder, five-spice powder, baking soda, and salt into medium bowl.

3 Combine granulated sugar, egg, egg white, oil, and ginger in large bowl. Add flour mixture and stir just until combined. Stir in pineapple and reserved liquid, carrots, and raisins. Scrape batter into prepared pan. Bake until toothpick inserted into centre comes out clean, 25–30 minutes. Cool cake in pan on rack 10 minutes. Remove cake from pan and cool completely on rack.

4 Beat cream cheese, confectioners' sugar, and milk in medium bowl just until blended and smooth. Spread on top of cooled cake. Cut into 12 squares.

Per serving (1 square): 171 Cal, 3 g Total Fat, 0 g Sat Fat, 0 g Trans Fat, 19 mg Chol, 304 mg Sod, 33 g Carb, 18 g Sugar, 1 g Fib, 4 g Prot, 62 mg Calc.

five-spice carrot cake

cranberry tea scones

serves 6

per serving

- **125 ml (½ cup) all-purpose flour**
- **125 ml (½ cup) whole wheat pastry flour**
- **7 ml (1½ tsp) baking powder**
- **2 ml (½ tsp) salt**
- **15 ml (1 Tbsp) + 5 ml (1 tsp) sugar**
- **30 ml (2 Tbsp) unsalted butter, melted and cooled**
- **60 ml (¼ cup) + 5 ml (1 tsp) low-fat (1%) milk**
- ▲ **45 ml (3 Tbsp) fat-free egg substitute**
- **7 ml (1½ tsp) finely grated orange zest**
- **75 ml (⅓ cup) dried cranberries**

1 Preheat oven to 230°C (450°F).

2 Combine all-purpose flour, whole wheat pastry flour, baking powder, salt, and 15 ml (1 Tbsp) sugar in medium bowl. With fork, stir in butter until mixture resembles coarse crumbs.

3 Combine 60 ml (¼ cup) milk, egg substitute, and orange zest in small bowl. Stir milk mixture into flour mixture just until blended. Stir in cranberries.

4 Gather dough into ball and knead on lightly floured surface until fairly smooth, about 30 seconds. Pat dough into 1.25-cm (½-in) thick circle. Brush with remaining 5 ml (1 tsp) milk and sprinkle with remaining 5 ml (1 tsp) sugar. Cut into 6 wedges; transfer to baking sheet. Bake until golden brown, 10–12 minutes. Serve warm.

Per serving (1 scone): 137 Cal, 4 g Total Fat, 3 g Sat Fat, 0 g Trans Fat, 11 mg Chol, 348 mg Sod, 23 g Carb, 7 g Sugar, 1 g Fib, 3 g Prot, 49 mg Calc.

stay on track

These scones also make a terrific breakfast; serve them with 250 ml (1 cup) plain fat-free Greek yogourt topped with your favourite fruit for an additional ***3 PointsPlus*** value.

spiced pumpkin-mango loaf

serves 12

per serving

- 375 ml (1½ cups) all-purpose flour
- 75 ml (⅓ cup) packed dark brown sugar
- 5 ml (1 tsp) baking soda
- 5 ml (1 tsp) ground ginger
- 5 ml (1 tsp) cinnamon
- 2 ml (½ tsp) baking powder
- 1 ml (¼ tsp) ground cloves
- 1 ml (¼ tsp) salt
- ▲ 250 ml (1 cup) canned pumpkin purée
- 1 jar (250 ml [8 fl. oz]) mango chutney, large pieces chopped
- ▲ 1 large egg
- ▲ 3 large egg whites
- 75 ml (⅓ cup) vanilla low-fat yogourt
- 45 ml (3 Tbsp) vegetable oil

1 Preheat oven to 180°C (350°F). Spray 22.5 x 12.5-cm (9 x 5-in) loaf pan with nonstick spray.

2 Combine flour, brown sugar, baking soda, ginger, cinnamon, baking powder, cloves, and salt in large bowl. Stir together pumpkin, chutney, egg, egg whites, yogourt, and oil in small bowl. Add pumpkin mixture to flour mixture and stir just until combined.

3 Pour batter into prepared loaf pan and bake until toothpick inserted into centre comes out clean, 60–70 minutes. Cool bread in pan on rack about 10 minutes; remove from pan and cool completely on rack. Cut into 12 slices.

Per serving (1 slice): 192 Cal, 6 g Total Fat, 1 g Sat Fat, 0 g Trans Fat, 18 mg Chol, 422 mg Sod, 31 g Carb, 8 g Sugar, 1 g Fib, 4 g Prot, 38 mg Calc.

walnut-crunch bran muffins

serves 12

per serving

- 75 ml (5 Tbsp) packed dark brown sugar
- 45 ml (3 Tbsp) finely chopped walnuts
- ▲ 2 large eggs
- 310 ml (1¼ cups) bran cereal
- ▲ 250 ml (1 cup) fat-free buttermilk
- 30 ml (2 Tbsp) canola oil
- 30 ml (2 Tbsp) molasses
- 250 ml (1 cup) all-purpose flour
- 60 ml (¼ cup) toasted wheat germ
- 10 ml (2 tsp) baking powder
- 5 ml (1 tsp) cinnamon
- 2 ml (½ tsp) baking soda
- 1 ml (¼ tsp) salt
- ▲ 1 large pear, peeled, cored, and shredded

1 Preheat oven to 190°C (375°F). Spray nonstick 12-cup muffin pan with nonstick spray.

2 Mix 30 ml (2 Tbsp) brown sugar with walnuts in small bowl; set aside for topping.

3 Lightly beat eggs in large bowl. Add remaining 45 ml (3 Tbsp) brown sugar, bran cereal, buttermilk, oil, and molasses; let stand 5 minutes.

4 Meanwhile, combine flour, wheat germ, baking powder, cinnamon, baking soda, and salt in medium bowl. Stir flour mixture into cereal mixture just until blended. Stir in pear.

5 Spoon batter into prepared muffin cups. Sprinkle evenly with walnut topping. Bake until toothpick inserted into muffin centres comes out clean, 20–25 minutes. Cool in pan on rack 5 minutes. Remove muffins from pan and cool completely on rack.

Per serving (1 muffin): 157 Cal, 5 g Total Fat, 1 g Sat Fat, 0 g Trans Fat, 36 mg Chol, 255 mg Sod, 26 g Carb, 12 g Sugar, 2 g Fib, 4 g Prot, 63 mg Calc.

dark chocolate soufflés with raspberry sauce

serves 4

per serving

- 20 ml (4 tsp) sugar
- 60 g (2 oz) semisweet chocolate, coarsely chopped
- ▲ 15 ml (1 Tbsp) skim milk
- 1 large egg yolk
- 15 ml (1 Tbsp) all-purpose flour
- ▲ 2 large egg whites
- 1 ml (¼ tsp) cream of tartar
- ▲ 375 ml (1½ cups) fresh or unsweetened frozen raspberries
- 10 ml (2 tsp) vanilla extract
- 5 ml (1 tsp) fresh lemon juice

1 Preheat oven to 200°C (400°F). Spray 4 (125-ml [4-fl. oz]) ramekins with nonstick spray and coat each with 2 ml (½ tsp) sugar.

2 Place chocolate and milk in medium microwavable bowl. Microwave on High until chocolate is melted, 30–40 seconds, stopping and stirring about every 10 seconds. Whisk in yolk and flour until smooth. Set aside until cool.

3 With electric mixer, beat egg whites and cream of tartar in medium bowl until soft peaks form. Sprinkle with remaining 10 ml (2 tsp) sugar and beat until glossy, about 2 minutes longer. Gently fold beaten egg whites into chocolate mixture. Spoon batter into prepared ramekins. Place cups on baking sheet and bake until soufflés are puffed and dried on top, 10–15 minutes.

4 Meanwhile, to make sauce, combine raspberries, vanilla, and lemon juice in blender and puree. Strain mixture into bowl through wire mesh sieve, pressing with rubber spatula; discard seeds. Serve soufflés with sauce.

Per serving (1 soufflé with about 60 ml [¼ cup] sauce): 162 Cal, 6 g Total Fat, 3 g Sat Fat, 0 g Trans Fat, 53 mg Chol, 32 mg Sod, 25 g Carb, 15 g Sugar, 6 g Fib, 5 g Prot, 33 mg Calc.

honey rice pudding with fruit

honey rice pudding with fruit

serves 4

per serving

- ▲ **500 ml (2 cups) skim milk**
- **375 ml (1½ cups) cooked long-grain white rice**
- **30 ml (2 Tbsp) honey**
- ▲ **1 large orange, peeled and chopped**
- ▲ **2 kiwifruit, peeled and chopped**
- **10 ml (2 tsp) grated orange zest**
- **2 ml (½ tsp) vanilla extract**

1 Bring milk, rice, and honey to boil in medium saucepan. Reduce heat and simmer, uncovered, stirring often, until pudding is thick and creamy, about 15 minutes.

2 Meanwhile, combine orange and kiwifruit in medium bowl. Set aside.

3 Remove pudding from heat and stir in orange zest and vanilla. Let stand at room temperature to cool slightly. Serve pudding warm, or cover and refrigerate until chilled, about 2 hours. Serve with orange mixture.

Per serving (125 ml [½ cup] pudding and 125 ml [½ cup] orange mixture): 198 Cal, 1 g Total Fat, 0 g Sat Fat, 0 g Trans Fat, 2 mg Chol, 54 mg Sod, 43 g Carb, 23 g Sugar, 3 g Fib, 7 g Prot, 193 mg Calc.

for your information

Love raisins? Add 60 ml (¼ cup) raisins to the pudding in Step 1 and increase the per-serving ***PointsPlus*** value by ***1***. Grate the orange zest from the orange before peeling and chopping it.

chocolate turtle ice-cream cake

serves 16

per serving

16 reduced-fat chocolate sandwich cookies, crushed

1 L (2 pints) chocolate fat-free frozen yogourt, slightly softened

500 ml (1 pint) vanilla fat-free frozen yogourt, slightly softened

125 ml (½ cup) chopped pecans

125 ml (½ cup) fat-free caramel topping, heated

1 Press crumbs evenly over bottom of 22.5-cm (9-inch) springform pan.

2 Spoon 1 pint chocolate frozen yogourt over cookie crumbs, spreading to form even layer. Freeze until firm, about 20 minutes. Repeat with vanilla frozen yogourt, and then remaining 1 pint chocolate frozen yogourt. Wrap pan tightly in foil and freeze until completely frozen, at least 6 hours or up to 1 week.

3 Remove foil from pan. Sprinkle pecans evenly over cake, pressing lightly to adhere. Run knife around sides of cake; remove pan sides. Using large knife, cut cake into 16 wedges, rinsing knife under hot water between cuts and shaking off excess water. Place cake on plates and drizzle evenly with caramel topping. Serve at once.

Per serving (1/16 of cake and (7 ml [1½ tsp]) caramel topping): 189 Cal, 4 g Total Fat, 1 g Sat Fat, 0 g Trans Fat, 6 mg Chol, 154 mg Sod, 33 g Carb, 22 g Sugar, 1 g Fib, 5 g Prot, 120 mg Calc.

stay on track

This delicious, easy-to-make cake can make birthdays or other celebrations a little sweeter and healthier. Serve it along with a big bowl of fruit salad and you'll be less tempted to take seconds.

gingersnap ice-cream sandwiches

serves 4

per serving

30 ml (2 Tbsp) sweetened flaked coconut, finely chopped

30 ml (2 Tbsp) finely chopped pecans

125 ml (½ cup) vanilla fat-free ice cream

8 gingersnap cookies

1 Combine coconut and pecans on sheet of wax paper.

2 Place small baking sheet in freezer. Place 30 ml (2 Tbsp) ice cream on 1 cookie. Top with second cookie, gently pressing down. Working quickly, roll cookie edges in coconut mixture to coat; then transfer to baking sheet. Repeat with remaining ice cream, cookies, and coconut mixture to make 4 sandwich cookies. Wrap each sandwich in plastic wrap and freeze until firm, about 1 hour. Ice-cream sandwiches may be frozen up to 3 months.

Per serving **(1 sandwich): 117 Cal, 5 g Total Fat, 1 g Sat Fat, 0 g Trans Fat, 1 mg Chol, 112 mg Sod, 18 g Carb, 7 g Sugar, 2 g Fib, 2 g Prot, 34 mg Calc.**

mocha malts

under 20 minutes • serves 4

per serving

375 ml (1½ cups) coffee fat-free ice cream
▲ 375 ml (1½ cups) skim milk
30 ml (2 Tbsp) malt powder
30 ml (2 Tbsp) chocolate syrup

Combine ice cream, milk, malt powder, and syrup in blender. Process on high speed until smooth and frothy. Pour into 4 tall slim glasses and serve with extra-long straws.

Per serving (175 ml [¾ cup]): 189 Cal, 3 g Total Fat, 2 g Sat Fat, 0 g Trans Fat, 9 mg Chol, 150 mg Sod, 37 g Carb, 27 g Sugar, 4 g Fib, 6 g Prot, 205 mg Calc.

for your information

The whole family will enjoy this refreshing frozen drink. If you're serving it to young children, you can substitute chocolate ice cream for the coffee ice cream.

clockwise from top:
mocha malts;
mocha-walnut biscotti, page 219;
gingersnap ice-cream
sandwiches, page 213

pineapple foster with yogourt

under 20 minutes • serves 2

per serving

- 5 ml (1 tsp) unsalted butter
- ▲ 375 ml (1½ cups) cubed fresh pineapple
- 20 ml (4 tsp) dark rum
- 20 ml (4 tsp) brown sugar
- ▲ 250 ml (1 cup) plain fat-free Greek yogourt

1 Melt butter in medium nonstick skillet over medium heat. Add pineapple and cook, stirring often, until softened and lightly browned, about 8 minutes. Add rum and brown sugar. Cook until sugar dissolves and mixture is syrupy, about 2 minutes.

2 Divide yogourt between 2 dishes and spoon pineapple mixture evenly over each serving. Serve at once.

Per serving (125 ml [½ cup] yogourt with about 175 ml [¾ cup] pineapple mixture): 196 Cal, 2 g Total Fat, 1 g Sat Fat, 0 g Trans Fat, 10 mg Chol, 47 mg Sod, 30 g Carb, 26 g Sugar, 2 g Fib, 11 g Prot, 100 mg Calc.

baked apples with ricotta

serves 2

- ▲ 2 baking apples, such as Rome, McIntosh, or Gala
- ▲ 1 orange, peeled and diced
- 1 ml (¼ tsp) apple pie spice or cinnamon
- ▲ 150 ml (⅔ cup) low fat ricotta cheese

1 Preheat oven to 180°C (350°F).

2 With apple corer or melon baller, hollow out core of apples without cutting through to bottom. Peel top half of apples. Trim bottoms if necessary so apples stand upright. Place apples in small shallow baking dish.

3 Stir together orange and spice in small bowl. Spoon 15 ml (1 Tbsp) of orange mixture into cavity of each apple; spoon remaining orange mixture into bottom of dish.

4 Bake, occasionally spooning pan juices over apples, until apples are tender when pierced with knife, 40–45 minutes. Serve apples warm or at room temperature with pan juices and ricotta.

Per serving (1 apple, [30 ml (2 Tbsp)] pan juices, and 75 ml [⅓ cup] ricotta): 102 Cal, 2 g Total Fat, 1 g Sat Fat, 0 g Trans Fat, 13 mg Chol, 99 mg Sod, 18 g Carb, 13 g Sugar, 3 g Fib, 5 g Prot, 86 mg Calc.

stay on track

Unsweetened baked apples make a healthful dessert, and the addition of the ricotta cheese makes them more satisfying. They're packed with fibre and protein, so they'll even make a filling breakfast. If you like you can double the recipe; just make sure you use a baking dish large enough to hold the apples in a single layer.

strawberries with caramel fondue

under 20 minutes • serves 4

per serving

- 45 ml (3 Tbsp) white chocolate chips
- ▲ 30 ml (2 Tbsp) light cream (5% M.F.)
- ▲ 45 ml (3 Tbsp) fat-free caramel topping
- ▲ 750 ml (3 cups) fresh strawberries, stems removed

1 Combine chocolate chips and cream in small microwavable bowl. Microwave on High 20–30 seconds, just until mixture begins to simmer. Stir until mixture is smooth. Add caramel topping and stir until blended.

2 Transfer fondue to small serving dish. Serve warm with strawberries for dipping.

Per serving (22 ml [1½ Tbsp] fondue and 175 ml [¾ cup] strawberries): 123 Cal, 3 g Total Fat, 2 g Sat Fat, 0 g Trans Fat, 4 mg Chol, 66 mg Sod, 23 g Carb, 21 g Sugar, 2 g Fib, 2 g Prot, 51 mg Calc.

for your information

You can use any fruit that is in season for dipping. Try fresh pineapple or cantaloupe cubes, or apple or pear wedges.

mocha-walnut biscotti

serves 12

per serving

- 175 ml (¾ cup) all-purpose flour
- 45 ml (3 Tbsp) unsweetened cocoa
- 10 ml (2 tsp) instant espresso powder
- 10 ml (2 tsp) cinnamon
- 2 ml (½ tsp) baking powder
- 1 ml (¼ tsp) salt
- 125 ml (½ cup) sugar
- ▲ 1 large egg
- 2 ml (½ tsp) vanilla extract
- 75 ml (⅓ cup) coarsely chopped walnuts

1 Preheat oven to 180°C (350°F). Line baking sheet with foil and spray lightly with nonstick spray.

2 Sift flour, cocoa, espresso powder, cinnamon, baking powder, and salt into medium bowl. Whisk together sugar, egg, and vanilla in small bowl. Add egg mixture to flour mixture and stir just until dough forms. Fold in walnuts.

3 Gather dough with lightly floured hands and transfer to lightly floured surface. Roll into log about 5 cm (2 in) in diameter and 20 cm (8 in) long. Transfer log to baking sheet and flatten gently until it is about 2 cm (¾-inch) high. Bake until firm, 20–25 minutes. Reduce oven temperature to 150°C (300°F).

4 Transfer log to cutting board and cool about 5 minutes. With serrated knife, cut into 12 (0.6-cm [¼-in]) slices. Arrange slices on baking sheet. Bake biscotti 10 minutes, then turn over and bake until dry and slightly crisp, about 10 minutes longer. Transfer to rack and cool completely. The biscotti will continue to crisp as they cool. Store in airtight container for up to 2 weeks.

Per serving (1 biscotti): 81 Cal, 3 g Total Fat, 0 g Sat Fat, 0 g Trans Fat, 18 mg Chol, 77 mg Sod, 14 g Carb, 6 g Sugar, 1 g Fib, 2 g Prot, 16 mg Calc.

clementine madeleines

serves 16

per serving

- ▲ **1 clementine or tangerine**
- ▲ **1 large egg white**
- **45 ml (3 Tbsp) water**
- **60 ml (4 Tbsp) confectioners' sugar**
- **1 package (240 g [8½ oz]) corn muffin mix (without added butter)**
- **30 ml (2 Tbsp) unsalted butter, melted**

1 Preheat oven to 190°C (375°F). Spray 48 mini–madeleine molds with nonstick spray.

2 Grate 5 ml (1 tsp) zest from clementine; squeeze 30 ml (2 Tbsp) juice. Whisk together egg white and water in medium bowl. Stir in clementine zest and juice and 30 ml (2 Tbsp) confectioners' sugar. Add muffin mix and melted butter; stir just until combined.

3 Spoon batter into prepared madeleine molds, filling two-thirds full. Bake until edges are golden and tops spring back when lightly pressed in centre, about 8 minutes. Immediately invert madeleines on racks and let cool. Sprinkle with remaining 30 ml (2 Tbsp) confectioners' sugar just before serving.

Per serving (3 mini-madeleines): 86 Cal, 3 g Total Fat, 1 g Sat Fat, 0 g Trans Fat, 4 mg Chol, 171 mg Sod, 13 g Carb, 5 g Sugar, 1 g Fib, 1 g Prot, 11 mg Calc.

heavenly oat bars

serves 12

per serving

- 175 ml (¾ cup) quick-cooking oats
- 60 ml (¼ cup) ground flaxseed
- 30 ml (2 Tbsp) white whole wheat flour
- 125 ml (½ cup) dried cranberries
- 125 ml (½ cup) dried apricots, chopped
- 60 ml (¼ cup) pecans
- 30 ml (2 Tbsp) dry-roasted sunflower seeds
- 2 ml (½ tsp) cinnamon
- Pinch salt
- ▲ 60 ml (¼ cup) fat-free egg substitute
- 45 ml (3 Tbsp) maple syrup

1 Preheat oven to 180°C (350°F). Line 20-cm (8-in) square baking pan with foil, extending foil over rim of pan by 5 cm (2 in). Spray foil with nonstick spray.

2 Combine oats, flaxseed, flour, cranberries, apricots, pecans, sunflower seeds, cinnamon, and salt in food processor; process until finely chopped. Add egg substitute and maple syrup. Pulse until the mixture is well blended.

3 Spoon fruit mixture into prepared pan and press to level. Bake until firm and browned along edges, about 20 minutes. Let cool completely in pan on wire rack. Lift from pan using foil. Cut into 12 bars.

Per serving (1 bar): 106 Cal, 4 g Total Fat, 0 g Sat Fat, 0 g Trans Fat, 0 mg Chol, 21 mg Sod, 17 g Carb, 9 g Sugar, 2 g Fib, 2 g Prot, 15 mg Calc.

stay on track

Oats are an excellent food to eat more of any time of the day, particularly when you're trying to lose weight. Oatmeal is high in soluble fibre, a type of fibre that slows digestion, helping you feel full longer.

cantaloupe-lime frosty

under 20 minutes • serves 1

per serving

- ▲ **250 ml (1 cup) cantaloupe cubes**
- **125 ml (½ cup) ice cubes**
- **60 ml (¼ cup) light cranberry-raspberry juice**
- **22 ml (1½ Tbsp) seedless raspberry all-fruit spread**
- **5 ml (1 tsp) lime juice**

Place all ingredients in blender and puree. Pour mixture into tall glass and serve at once.

Per serving (375 ml [1½ cups]): 89 Cal, 0 g Total Fat, 0 g Sat Fat, 0 g Trans Fat, 0 mg Chol, 31 mg Sod, 22 g Carb, 20 g Sugar, 1 g Fib, 1 g Prot, 24 mg Calc.

for your information

For a festive touch you can garnish the rim of your glass with a strawberry or a pineapple wedge.

chilled honeydew-mint soup

serves 2

per serving

- ▲ ¼ honeydew melon, cubed (about 625 ml [2½ cups])
- 22 ml (1½ Tbsp) honey
- 2 ml (½ tsp) grated lime zest
- 15 ml (1 Tbsp) lime juice
- 15 ml (1 Tbsp) chopped fresh mint
- ▲ 60 ml (¼ cup) finely chopped honeydew

Combine honeydew cubes, honey, lime zest and juice, and mint in blender; process until pureed. Transfer to container, cover, and refrigerate until chilled, at least 2 hours. Serve garnished with chopped honeydew.

Per serving (250 ml [1 cup]): 101 Cal, 0 g Total Fat, 0 g Sat Fat, 0 g Trans Fat, 0 mg Chol, 27 mg Sod, 26 g Carb, 25 g Sugar, 1 g Fib, 1 g Prot, 12 mg Calc.

recipes by *PointsPlus* value

6
PointsPlus
value

7
PointsPlus
value

8
PointsPlus
value

Recipes that work with the Simply Filling technique

Index

*Page numbers in *italics* indicate photographs.

C

D

H

I

J

K

L

S

T

U

Dry and Liquid Measurement Equivalents

If you are converting the recipes in this book to metric measurements, use the following chart as a guide.

TEASPOONS	TABLESPOONS	CUPS	FLUID OUNCES
3 teaspoons	1 tablespoon		½ fluid ounce
6 teaspoons	2 tablespoons	⅛ cup	1 fluid ounce
8 teaspoons	2 tablespoons plus 2 teaspoons	⅙ cup	
12 teaspoons	4 tablespoons	¼ cup	2 fluid ounces
15 teaspoons	5 tablespoons	⅓ cup minus 1 teaspoon	
16 teaspoons	5 tablespoons plus 1 teaspoon	⅓ cup	
18 teaspoons	6 tablespoons	¼ cup plus 2 tablespoons	3 fluid ounces
24 teaspoons	8 tablespoons	½ cup	4 fluid ounces
30 teaspoons	10 tablespoons	½ cup plus 2 tablespoons	5 fluid ounces
32 teaspoons	10 tablespoons plus 2 teaspoons	⅔ cup	
36 teaspoons	12 tablespoons	¾ cup	6 fluid ounces
42 teaspoons	14 tablespoons	1 cup minus 2 tablespoons	7 fluid ounces
45 teaspoons	15 tablespoons	1 cup minus 1 tablespoon	
48 teaspoons	16 tablespoons	1 cup	8 fluid ounces

OVEN TEMPERATURE			
250°F	120°C	400°F	200°C
275°F	140°C	425°F	220°C
300°F	150°C	450°F	230°C
325°F	160°C	475°F	250°C
350°F	180°C	500°F	260°C
375°F	190°C	525°F	270°C

Note: Measurement of less than ⅛ teaspoon is considered a dash or a pinch. Metric volume measurements are approximate.

VOLUME	
¼ teaspoon	1 millilitre
½ teaspoon	2 millilitres
1 teaspoon	5 millilitres
1 tablespoon	15 millilitres
2 tablespoons	30 millilitres
3 tablespoons	45 millilitres
¼ cup	60 millilitres
⅓ cup	80 millilitres
½ cup	120 millilitres
⅔ cup	160 millilitres
¾ cup	175 millilitres
1 cup	240 millilitres
1 quart	950 millilitres

LENGTH	
1 inch	25 millimetres
1 inch	2.5 centimetres

WEIGHT	
1 ounce	30 grams
¼ pound	115 grams
½ pound	225 grams
1 pound	450 grams